C000092519

Secret Fertility Club

Amelia McCloskey

Isbn: 9978-1-914399-92-3

Printed and bound in Great Britain by Clays Ltd, Elcograf S.p.A.

SPARSILE
BOOKS

To the four little angels who left footprints on my heart and blessed me with their presence even for a short while, which gave me hope that all is possible.

And

To everyone in the secret fertility club.
I see you, I feel you, I hold your hand in solidarity with you as I am you.

You are not alone in this.

To all,

I hope my story inspires you, brings peace, hope and healing and more importantly encourages you to speak up, use your voice to share your story too as your story is powerful and can heal another.

SYNOPSIS

After years of trying to conceive, Amelia learnt she was unknowingly pregnant when an ectopic pregnancy ruptured in the middle of the night. She was rushed into surgery twelve hours later, nearly losing her life. Later, she went on to suffer a further ectopic pregnancy, followed by three rounds of IVF and two miscarriages. Follow her emotional journey of strength, hope and loss as you delve into the secret world of the fertility club.

DISCLAIMER

In this book I have tried to give an honest and personal account of my experiences with infertility. My intention is not to give medical advice, I am not a doctor, but to make my audience aware that you are not alone in any fertility struggles you might face.

These are my personal experiences told from my perspective and naturally with the bias of my own viewpoint. In order to respect the privacy of individuals, names have been changed and, in some cases, a character may represent an amalgam of different individuals. Some locations and times have also been altered.

PROLOGUE

*'Let your hopes, not your hurts,
shape your future'*

As I sit here writing this, I'm currently trying to stop my head from doing a 360⁰ exorcist-style spin from all the dreaded test results and hoops my partner, *Peter (not his real name. Names that have been changed are signified by a *), and I are having to jump through for the umpteenth time. We're just trying to make it to the next small milestone—a rise in hCG (the level of pregnancy hormone in the blood that shows how the pregnancy is developing)—and at the same time we feel grateful for even a tiny amount of hCG in the first place.

I'll explain: we're currently in our third cycle of IVF with a top clinic in Greece (more on this later). I received a BFP (big fat positive) test result over a fortnight ago and have to be closely monitored back in the UK to see if this pregnancy is 'viable'. In layman's terms: is it going to go the distance?

My hCG levels started at 41.8 ml then on to 124 ml, which are considered low, but they are climbing which is a good sign; we fertility warriors take any little positives we can in this journey! I find myself constantly Googling *'recommended hCG level 14 days post transfer'* and *'success stories of pregnancies with low hCG'.* There are lots of variations where Peter and I can find positive stories of hope to cling to. Although we do also find ourselves being scare-mongered with the negatives, and there's plenty of those out there on the forums! I trawl the internet and the many forums I've signed up to, trying to find the positive answer of hope I'm looking for, even though I should, as everyone says...ring my DOCTOR. But why ring my doctor when I can first spend hours of time looking through other people's answers before coming to the same conclusion of, 'Yeah, I should probably just get a doctor's opinion on this!'

Yes, I know, I know it's better to stay off these forums as everyone's journey is different and every pregnancy is unique, but I JUST CAN'T HELP IT! And I'm completely sure my readers can all relate! Because all I want to do is talk and share with others in the same position, Every fertility warrior in this secret club has their own story to tell, which is why I want to share mine.

Reasons for sharing:

1. Because I'm going out of my mind waiting on more blood tests to see if I'm going to finally be blessed with a baby, or if my hopes and dreams will be dashed again. Writing my journey is my form of therapy.

2. I want to help others by sharing my story, my triumphs, heartbreaks, trials and tribulations, as no one understands better than the fertility warriors who have been through (or are still going through) this journey themselves.

I decided to call this book the *Secret Fertility Club* because when someone finds out they're challenged in the fertility area they automatically join the secret fertility club. (I'm avoiding using the word 'infertility' as it's a cold, horrible word: we're just a bit more challenged in the area of fertility than some others). I call it secret as many don't like to admit, share or talk about fertility issues with those close to them, There is still such a stigma attached to it. So we post online using pseudonyms and we share our questions, stories, heartaches and triumphs with others. As far as I'm concerned everyone who is in this club is a warrior who has battled time and again for what they desire.

These fertility warriors are also the smartest bloody women I know. They seem to quickly learn how to be scientific IVF/fertility experts, which you will see when you read how they dissect each other's lab reports. They can tell you all the hormone, sperm and blood result percentages. They'll tell you exactly what the scientific meaning is, what meds they recommend you should take or what you should question with your doctor. I'm not kidding, it astounds me how much they learn on this journey! They're also the strongest, most compassionate, resilient humans I've ever come across, and for that reason alone it makes me feel proud to be a part of this club.

I toyed with the idea of keeping my name private or using a pseudonym. But I decided to use my actual name as I'm proud of the difficult journey I've been on, and feel it's important for each and every one of us to use our voice and share our experiences to help others. It's important to end the stigma surrounding fertility issues when one in seven couples have difficulty conceiving.

ONE
Where It All Began: Trying To Conceive (TTC) Naturally

'Even miracles take a little time'

So far to date, I've had two ectopic pregnancies, both fallopian tubes removed, one miscarriage and three rounds of IVF. I have been on this rollercoaster fertility journey for around five years now.

I didn't want kids growing up, and throughout my twenties I was always focused on my career in the music business. First as a singer, then I studied music, got into song writing and spent a few months interning at record labels in London and some top recording studios in LA. After that, I became a vocal coach, setting up my own business and developing and managing the careers of other artists. I had my own studio premises and staff to manage, so getting ahead in my career was always my top priority. I still work in the business today, running two award-winning companies within the music industry.

I had a few relationships when I was younger. My first relationship lasted ten months which seems like an eternity when you're twelve. He was my first proper love and we were inseparable. We were the model school couple until he got expelled (I always did have a thing for the older, bad boys) and then things pretty much fell apart from there.

In my teens the only thing I was particularly interested in were boys, make-up, singing and partying. It was a wild, free time that involved many dance festivals, clubs and then turning up to GCSEs having just come back from some dance festival or other still feeling the effects of whatever was taken at the event. I have no idea how we even managed to get into most of these clubs and festivals as we definitely did not look eighteen and our IDs were just out of the back of some random magazine that we sent off for; they couldn't have looked any faker!

There was a lot of cheating involved in my earlier relationships. They were pretty wild times with no-one bothering to use protection, especially in the longer-term relationships such as the one I found myself in. There just wasn't the education and awareness surrounding the potential for picking up STDs. Pregnancies yes, but STDs no. Also, when you're young, you think you're invincible and bad stuff happens to other people, not you.

There was one particular two-timing situation (which is what we called it back then) that went on for a while and which broke my heart as it was close to home and took me a long time to recover from. After it, I struggled with trust for a long-time. It's a familiar scenario, one many people have to go through as a learning experience. The difference is mine nearly ended up taking my life. This happened later on down the line and I'll explain it all later.

I did go on to have a few serious relationships that lasted around five years with live-in partners, some ended amicably and some not, but by my 20's I was so focused on getting ahead in my career that kids weren't really something I was interested in pursuing so it was only when I met *Peter that I discovered the effects of having chosen unsuitable partners and lived a wild youth had caught up with me.

I was in my thirties when I got together with Peter. He was working for me when I was managing artists, although we disliked each other at first. Even though he was always good at his job, I found him arrogant, pompous and rude. He slammed the door behind him when he came for an interview with me. I was with other applicants, and we were running behind, so I told my assistant to tell him to wait outside, which he clearly didn't like so I said, 'Well, he can wait out there longer then if he wants to act like that!' That's typically how our relationship has been since—a bit of a power struggle as we're both quite strong characters.

Perhaps unfairly, I found him quite boring when we first met, as I was a single girl who loved to go out, socialise and party and although I didn't know much about him, I knew he definitely wasn't a party animal like I was. But, as I said, he was good at his job and the artists liked him. Over time we got to know each other, something clicked and we fell for each other. We had deep, meaningful conversations and found we had a lot in common with our work ethic, personalities and the fact that we both wanted a family. I began to see him in a new light.

I had also changed over time and was looking for a quieter life. I was fed up being single. My work just wasn't enough to complete me anymore. I hadn't even been concerned about having kids most of my life and then boom! Hello, baby boiler alert! All of a sudden, I was noticing babies everywhere and my biological clock was ticking loudly inside my head.

In addition to this, the media is forever reminding us not to waste time. Magazines and social media headlines are always about which celebrity is now pregnant or giving birth in case we might have forgotten—for just a second—that we're not. We're given constant reminders—which actually reminds me to take my fertility shot now!

Once I knew I wanted to have kids I talked it through with Peter and he felt the same: at an age now where he wanted to settle down. In a perfect world, that's all you'd need: two consenting adults, lots of fun trying, then the baby stork comes to deliver. If only! Once we had decided, I went into baby-making in the same way I treat any goal or anything in business. I go straight after it, full of determination and fire, full of positivity, try to control every aspect of it and work hard until I get results. If you don't see results straight away, try harder. (Yes, I can literally hear you laughing at me right now.)

I simply learnt the hard way that when you're TTC (trying to conceive) you cannot control a single thing. Nada. Which is a hard lesson for us high achievers who like to micromanage everything. The ONLY things I could control were my outlook and perspective. Before I'd learnt this hard lesson, I'd spent a whole year monitoring my ovulation and peeing on ovulation sticks. Once I started on this journey, I spent my life peeing on sticks (POAS). For those in the fertility club, everyone knows ovulation is the holy grail for all things related to baby-making. It's also highly likely when you're in this fertility club you'll also know exactly what day you ovulate. Then you base your WHOLE life around that day, the days leading up to it, and perhaps one or two days after.

I cancelled plans if it got in the way of my baby-making. I had sex in risqué areas when it was peak ovulation time (not a bad thing). But after a while, the sex became mechanical as we were just focused on TTC, which takes over the passion and the ability to just enjoy sex in the first place. My partner was knackered and it started to get in between us. We went at it like rabbits, hoping and praying this would be the cycle that created our baby. Sounds simple and fun, yet I soon learned it was one of the hardest and most mechanical things to achieve because it was completely out of my hands and all down to Mother Nature when TTC. I experienced frustration as I'd never known it. I even had a calendar on my fertility app where I would chart everything from my period date, cycle length, ovulation day, signs, symptoms, etc.

No one could prepare me for my journey into fertility, no matter how many books I read, people I talked to, forums I perused (which can become an obsession, if you know what I mean). I became an absolute expert in all the different stages of my cycle, down to what vaginal discharge is an indication of pregnancy and what it was supposed to look like (the good and helpful kind) through to knowing the exact different stages of my cycle and what it looked like in my underwear (the wet kind and the dry kind). I would say sorry for providing too much information (TMI) but fertility warriors know that there is no TMI in this club. I would also immerse myself in the world of motherhood and would look adoringly at babies on TV and in the street. I would talk for hours to mothers about babies, their pregnancy, birth and their experiences, whilst imagining what mine would be like and when it would be my turn.

T W O
Two-Week-Wait or
2WW (Death Row)

*'Everything comes to you at the
right moment, be patient'*

Although I swore that I would never let myself do it, that
I wouldn't get caught up in this whole 'baby drama', before
long I was spending countless hours happily wasting time
Googling every symptom, every twinge, every small possible sign. All primness went out of the window when
I joined the Secret Fertility Club and, before I knew it,
I was joining in debates about whether Jane's latest test
looked like a faint line on her pregnancy stick or if she
was, once again, wilfully imagining it, or if Rachel has hit
the pinnacle of the vaginal discharge snotty gloop, whilst
sharing my own pictures unashamedly online for debate.

I found myself checking the forums out to make
sure I wasn't missing anything out that could help even
in the tiniest way on the journey to baby heaven. After
I had completed yet another cycle that I had humped
my way through, I was now completely tuned in to my

body and thinking I could notice every cramp, sensitive breast, bloating, or slight nausea I experienced, convinced I was pregnant while waiting for the actual result on death row... Ahem, sorry, 2WW.

2WW is actually read as a 'two-week wait'. We call it this in the Secret Fertility Club as that's the time between ovulation and finding out if I was pregnant. During this time, I was completely relaxed, really focused, probably out having fun and generally really enjoying life. Hahahaha! Had you there. Of course not, I was on death row trying to stop myself being classed as insane and sectioned as I was completely out of my mind with worry, on a rollercoaster ride of emotions, unable to concentrate, wanting to stay busy yet not able to do anything at all, feeling scared that it hadn't worked again yet excited at the prospect of it and picturing my hopes and dreams with my baby, imagining the two lines on a pregnancy test, excitedly telling everyone and visualising the whole pregnancy which would go blissfully well and my partner and I would live happily ever after...!

I would also be Googling 'signs of implantation' and 'pregnancy symptoms', 'pregnancy vs PMS symptoms', along with 'period late by one day, am I pregnant?' 'How to boost pregnancy chances in 2WW' 'Tips of coping during 2WW', and these are only the tip of the iceberg. Going onto the forums where reading about how Kelly is going out of her mind during the 2WW because of roller-coaster emotions didn't actually help me to feel any better; it only made me feel worse reading others' struggles during this time. I wanted to read about the positive stories to give me hope, but at the same time I didn't want to hear them in case I received a negative result.

During this 2WW, it felt like I was in no man's land on a super-fast roller coaster with my emotions, desperate to get off but completely unable to. The difficult thing is, PMS symptoms mimic pregnancy symptoms and I can't even begin to tell you how many times I've thought I've been pregnant only to have my bubble burst when my period arrived...yet again. It was the most soul-destroying, sad, helpless wave of emotions I could feel when my period arrived.

You keep going through the same cycle over and over again of Day 1 countdown to ovulation, Day 14 ovulation, sex before and after for five days, two-week wait and then POAS to get a negative result. Rinse and Repeat. It eventually started to take its toll on me, especially when I had been living Groundhog Day like this for a few years. This is another reason why I call everyone in the secret fertility club, 'warriors', because it builds the kind of resilience and strength only a fertility warrior would understand.

THREE
Emotional Effects of TTC

'And you begin again, and sometimes you lose, sometimes you win but you begin again'

I found myself, after a year of getting nowhere, feeling depressed, frustrated and irritable over the whole thing, yet I wanted it so much that I couldn't give up. I felt so helpless, in a state of desperation that I found myself thinking:

'There must be something wrong with me.'

'I'm never going to get pregnant.'

'This only happens to other people, not me'

'Why is everyone else around me getting pregnant and I'm not?'

'What are they doing that I'm not?'

I watched every YouTube video, podcast and googled everything I possibly could to help boost my chances. I signed up and posted on every forum related to TTC. Even when I was travelling in my car, I listened to anything related to fertility and tips to help me conceive. At what point had I gone from a successful businesswoman into a nappy-obsessed, crazed baby lady? That thought made me feel even more depressed. I even googled, 'Does your period arriving a day early mean you're pregnant?' Knowing full well the answer!

Women can even have phantom pregnancies where they feel they have the same symptoms as pregnant women and are convinced they're pregnant even when they're not, due to the power of the mind. Thoughts can become real, the body mimicking what the mind truly believes so no wonder phantoms happen.

Luckily, I always knew I wasn't pregnant once my period arrived...although I'd still look up, 'Can you still be pregnant even if your period arrives?' Yes, I look back now with embarrassment, but unless you've been in this situation, which a lot of readers will have, you won't get where I'm coming from. Members of the secret fertility club will also be able to relate to having to face the number of people who are ready to give you advice on what worked for them when it came to getting pregnant—whether you want that advice or not! I started (laughably) by trying everyone's suggestions:

A.   Because at this stage
        you'll try anything

and

B.   It must work as it worked for them and she says her friend of a friend swears by it and she has five children...because *everyone* has the answer to your fertility issue!

Here are some of the suggestions I tried to follow:

- ❖ I tried to change my diet.

- ❖ I ate super healthy

- ❖ Then I tried a full-fat dairy

- ❖ A plant diet

- ❖ I ate more fish

- ❖ I ate more meat

- ❖ I gave up booze

- ❖ I gave up the cigarettes I smoked when I drank on weekends (this I know is helpful, but you try staying away from wine when you've had yet another disappointing, negative result).

❖ I put my legs in the air after sex or against the wall or did handstands (yes, I did do that. But only because my friend said she was doing it too and she said it helped, of course)

❖ I propped myself up with pillows underneath me

❖ I tried certain sex positions

❖ I drank raspberry tea

❖ I tried every vitamin under the sun including the super expensive ones

❖ I took cough syrup with guaifenesin when I didn't even have a cough as I read online it could help the quality of cervical mucous. This was the pinnacle of my madness

❖ I even considered kissing an iconic landmark that was rumoured to get you pregnant— crazy, I know. But at this stage, I was literally willing to try ANYTHING!

… the list is endless!

I then make pacts with God. I promised to be good, not touch cigarettes or alcohol any more, promised I would pray/go to church more, donate my kidneys, liver (if it's not battered) blood, anything you want in exchange for a *child*!

I started to confide in my friends about my struggle to conceive; none of them had kids at this stage but that soon changed over the years—which is another subject I'll get to. I remember speaking to my friend *Katie, yet again, about my fertility issues and explained to her how it was such a struggle for us as a couple to conceive while she and I were on a night out in London (she was single and was mainly into just dating guys for a night or two so not my target audience). As I saw her eyes glazing over as I, once again, spent an entire evening out discussing my ovaries—her words not mine—I re-alised I needed to do something about this and get to the bottom of why I just wasn't getting pregnant.

I was dying to know the answers but also equally terrified at the same time of being told I couldn't have children or something similar. Even more so, I needed to stop treating my friends as fertility doctors and counsellors rolled into one when they had no clue about this stuff anyway, and to actually enlist specialist help on this.

FOUR
Wrong Diagnosis

*'Forget all the reasons it won't work,
and believe the one reason it will'*

I always had a gut instinct deep down that I knew something was wrong in terms of my ability to get pregnant; call it women's intuition but somehow, we just know when something feels off. I'd always wondered how I'd gotten away with being careless in relationships about contraception and had never even come close to a scare! My periods had pretty much been on point and so I knew there wasn't an issue there. I was feeling deeply scared I might be told that I would never be able to have children, but either way, I needed to know to be able to prepare.

The thought of being told I was unable to have children was my biggest fear, and not only that, but I also feared that, if it were the case, then my partner would leave me for someone who was able to have babies. I didn't dwell on that for long as it was just too painful to think about. Although, in reality, I knew deep down that he would never do it, there's always that niggling possibility.

I made my first appointment with the doctor to discuss the issues I was having, completely unaware at this stage of the long, hard struggle ahead of me. My GP practice at the time only offered me appointments with male doctors which made going a bit harder as I was concerned a male doctor would dismiss my issues or wouldn't have the same empathy and compassion that a female doctor might show. Happily for me, my GP was actually kind about my concerns and sent me to the local hospital to have my hormone levels checked. Anyone who has gone through fertility testing on the NHS knows what a long, long journey this is, and that's just the wait for the paperwork to come back for your results which can take up to a month!

The thing with fertility is that it's a long WAIT-ING game. I would wait for my cycle to start, wait for ovulation, wait during 2WW, then repeat: wait for my appointment, which on the NHS, can take over four months just for a consultation, let alone any of the actual testing! Then I'd wait up to a month to hear what the result was, even for a simple blood test! I would actually describe it as literal torture of the mind—the endless waiting for something I wanted so much. I would have done anything, give up anything just to hear something. On the positive side, it really taught me patience and eventually...very eventually, the art of letting go. And it is an art, not giving up, just letting go the need for answers and to have results immediately, to let go of trying to have any control of the situation as I had zero control whatsoever. The minute I realised that and let go, the easier I could handle it.

I was always an impatient person until I started out on the fertility venture. I really latched on to the outcome at first, trying everything possible, obsessing over every single detail, not letting go until I had results. Perhaps it was the business side of me trying to control everything but it taught me the art of truly accepting the concept of going with the flow and not controlling anything. Simply because I couldn't!

It's Mother Nature that decides the outcome of fertility and whether I'll have a baby in my arms or not, even if it's mixed in with science. What I could control is chasing up the missing paperwork, incompetence, deliveries of meds when doing IVF, lack of communication issues, etc. I learned to be super organised with the dates of all my appointments, and this is vitally important for if/when you go through IVF! You will know exactly what I mean if you've been through it, which I'm sure many of you have!

Back to my hormones and my first fertility test. After my results FINALLY came back in the post about a month later, it turned out I had slightly elevated testosterone (so that's why I had some male traits in business then, such as dominance and aggression if people owed me money!). The doctor then prescribed me Metformin (whilst I waited nearly half a year for my first consultation appointment at the hospital to start further fertility testing) as he thought I had Polycystic Ovary Syndrome (PCOS)—which is crazy when you think about it. Metformin is a powerful drug that also treats type 2 diabetes and has some serious side effects

But, at the time, I was just happy to have a diagnosis and an answer to why I simply wasn't getting pregnant after so long trying naturally to conceive. So I happily started taking the tablets, convinced now all my problems were solved, and even happier when I read on the internet how it had acted like a fertility wonder drug for so many women! I was back on a high, ready to give it all my best shot again because I was going to be pregnant any day now with my new wonder drug! Oh, how wrong I was, and how the disappointments started arriving. All I was left with from this drug I was prescribed were awful side effects of diarrhoea and headaches!

FIVE
Our First Fertility Consultation

'Difficult roads lead to beautiful destinations'

Our appointment FINALLY arrived for our first consultation with fertility consultants at the local hospital on the NHS. We sat down with a nurse who asked us a lot of questions about our history and our sexual history (which can be quite embarrassing in front of your partner!). I discovered during these appointments that I had to repeat myself...a lot, as they never seem to share notes so it could be quite annoying at the very least and devastating when I had to keep repeating any lost information with the various consultants and doctors.

That day the consultant went through the recent results of my hormone test and was very surprised to see I'd been prescribed Metformin by my GP, as the results didn't indicate a prognosis of PCOS. She advised me to stop taking the Metformin tablets immediately, saying that I shouldn't have been prescribed it in the first place. Great! Now I felt worried. If they couldn't get my first diagnosis correct but would happily prescribe medication anyway, what else might they do? I was glad though not to have to take those nasty tablets...but what now? I was back at square one without a single clue what was wrong with me, or what was potentially wrong with Peter or perhaps both of us. I'd never felt so helpless and demoralised as I was at this point. So I did what we all do in these situations and went to the only place that felt familiar and friendly—my forums.

I felt really despondent with the news and knowing we were back at the beginning without answers. The pressure was starting to affect our relationship as I was getting really stressed out and depressed about constantly waiting for appointments, and trying so hard to get answers yet getting nowhere. Peter just didn't know how to fix the problem either. I knew deep down the issue was with me though, not him. I also didn't want us to start taking it out on each other with the constant struggle and pressure surrounding us on this emotional journey. My confidence started to suffer, and I really started to become insecure over my relationship, which didn't help matters, but I kept worrying that it'd be easier for him to find someone without these fertility issues.

The stress also affected our sex life negatively for a while, as I think we'd become burnt out with all our struggles. Neither of us knew at this stage that we still had such a long, difficult road ahead of us. On top of that, friends around me were now getting pregnant and inviting me to baby showers, but I just couldn't face it. I felt so jealous about women who only had to have sex, and boom, without trying, they were pregnant. It seemed everyone in the world was pregnant but me.

Of course, this wasn't actually the case, but it certainly felt like it! Every time a friend would announce a pregnancy, I just wanted to burst out crying and give up on it all or think 'what's the point?' It just hurt so much and then I would feel guilty for not being able to be around them or show up for them when they'd always been there for me.

But I thought I might just lose it and break down crying, and I definitely did not want to make a scene at a baby shower in front of others and have everyone say things like, '*Okay, let's escort out the weirdo!*' Of course, if I'd just explained myself then I know my friends would have understood. But I couldn't even bring myself to tell the truth, so I just avoided it. I couldn't even face the truth myself about how much I was now struggling with the thought of not being able to conceive and having no answers as to why.

Cowardly, I know, but self-preservation!

SIX
An Interesting Drive

*'You were given this mountain to
show others it can be moved'*

Our next appointment was a scan, for which we waited
another few months. Luckily, this came back completely
normal and I was feeling glad that, so far so good, nothing
problematic had shown itself, so potentially we could still
be able to conceive naturally. Peter and I were back on
track, we were communicating a lot better, and I made
sure to have a few nights out with friends to relax and let
my hair down to try to forget about the difficult journey
we were on.

We were still timing our cycles to keep trying naturally while we were under fertility care with the NHS. I
had read a million stories of spontaneous pregnancies
whilst you were going through fertility testing. Around
this time Peter had his sperm tested, which we decided
to do privately so it would be more efficient and the
results would come back quicker—or so you'd think!
We bought a urine pot and they told us to make sure

to bring in a sample that's as fresh as possible. Sounds simple, right? The morning we were due to set off at 8 a.m. to the clinic to get there for 9 a.m., my partner tried to ahem, 'do his business into the cup', at home before we left, (I was glad that he had something be all about him for once!) Sounds like an easy job, but he had to work in the morning and we'd run out of time, and so we decided we'd make our way towards the hospital and figure out a way to get it done somehow on the way!

Off in the car, we went into the morning traffic and before we knew it, we were round the corner from the hospital with no sample to hand in and only ten minutes until the appointment! What could we do? Peter found a quiet street to park in then he climbed into the back of the car (luckily it was an estate!). He got down to the task…ahem, at hand, whilst praying he wouldn't be caught and arrested for it! Imagine trying to explain that to the police officer! 'Sorry officer, my partner wasn't getting frisky at breakfast time during rush hour, he's doing a sperm sample for a fertility test!' Fair play to him though. He managed to do it and felt super proud of himself.

We dutifully handed it in and waited for the results, which we were told would take a few days, and we waited…and waited until we found out they had been misplaced. In the end, we had to chase that up, which took weeks! His result came back fine so he was super happy with that. (If you've ever tried to read a sperm diagnosis, it's baffling. Who knew there were so many components that make up sperm? Literally from the size, how quickly they move, how they're moving and what they look like. And volume!) Some fertility warriors would upload the results on the forums to get opinions—I didn't. Peter would've killed me! And others would weigh in with their full analysis and opinions. These fertility warriors are insanely clever at reading some of these results. You soon become an expert in all things fertility-related!

We were happy with having further answers and that Peter was in the clear, but that then meant the problem was now definitely with me, and we were still none the wiser as to what that problem was.

SEVEN
HSG Testing

*'When the world says give up, hope
whispers try one more time'*

A few months later, I received a letter from my local hospital booking a date for an HSG test, which is way easier to pronounce than *Hysterosalpingography*! Basically, this is a routine examination done by an X-ray where they check to see if the fallopian tubes are open and that the uterine cavity (uterus) is normal. Sounds simple, right? By this point, I was very much used to being prodded and poked, and had no fears of baring all with my feet in stirrups no matter who was in the room. There's no room for wilting wallflowers on this journey.

They said the procedure wouldn't take long so I felt very comfortable with the whole thing. I had to lie down on the hospital bed with a couple of female nurses around me and a huge X-ray machine. I tried to think of all things fluffy and lovely as they told me they'd be inserting a special-coloured dye inside me. If the dye flowed through the tubes and out the other end, then that would show that the tubes were functioning and working as they should and could also easily highlight any other potential issues. I was happy with that and felt no cause for concern.

They began to insert the dye, and OH My God! No word of a lie, all the blood rushed to my head and my face went bright red. I felt like my head was going to explode as I gripped on to the sides of the bed with all my might to stop myself from screaming out in agony at the top of my lungs. It was hands down one of the most painful experiences I've ever experienced.

The nurses were trying to soothe and comfort me, but I just wanted it to stop immediately. At some point, it became clear to me this was not normal. Surely it's not supposed to be this painful! They didn't say anything to me during the test to indicate if they'd discovered any-thing. They just told me to get dressed and that I would receive the results in the post soon. (Yeah, in a month's time more like, while I agonised over the delay!) I went home afterwards feeling very sorry for myself and started googling 'HSG experiences' and began read-ing others' experiences. Turns out the responses from others having the procedure were a mixture—as always! The majority of people didn't find it painful, and they didn't have an issue with their tubes. It seems the ones who did find it painful, had blockages with their tubes. This confirmed in my mind further that there must be something wrong with me, as I'd predicted.

However, I'd also been informed that women could be super fertile after having the dye test as the liquid helped to give the tubes a bit of a clean, so I was certain to make use of that lucky strike.

EIGHT
My First Surgery

*'Everyone you meet is fighting a battle
you know nothing about. Be Kind'*

Before I'd taken a train to destination fertility, I'd never had surgery as I'd never had a reason to, luckily. I'd always been, for the most part, pretty healthy. It had been a few months since my nightmare of a fallopian tube horror experience during the testing procedure and I had received my monthly letter from the NHS outlining my ~~fallopian failure~~ ahem, 'fallopian tube issues with my fertility'.

The letter had stated that they had discovered blockages with my fallopian tubes. My left tube was the most damaged and the right tube severely impaired though the dye was still passing through slowly. Before any of this even started, I'd never even given my fallopian tubes a second thought! They were just two neatly styled flutes tucked away, seemingly doing their job of delivering eggs or disposing of them if I wasn't having sex or wanting the stork to visit. And that was that!

I hadn't even given any of my reproductive organs much notice before I started fertility testing. But looking back I did have horrific seven-day periods that would invade me and my personal space every month. I never even gave much thought to the fact my periods were ridiculously painful and heavy at the time. I'd often suffered from painful tummy cramps too, but I assumed this was normal.

It's not really the kind of thing that's discussed amongst your friends: 'um, do you prefer light, regular sanitary pads or full-on nappies for your periods?' Hell no! The less we think about them the better was always my motto so I had nothing to compare my experience with. Also, every woman has painful periods, right? That's why they have adverts for period pain relief and images of women with blankets and hot water bottles on the sofa curled up with a huge slice of cake as big as your head! Or is that just me?

Jokes aside though, my pain during a period would literally be radiating from my front tummy, back and down my legs so much that I could barely walk! Yet, I still thought this was normal! Eventually, the pain would show itself during other times of my cycle too and was starting to become a more permanent fixture. I was glad to know that finally an issue had been pinpointed to a certain area; my tubes were blocked or partially blocked, but this was also at the same time very worrying for my fertility and my ability to conceive.

My letter from the NHS stated that I was due to undergo a laparoscopy (keyhole) surgery to check for endometritis as they thought that endometritis could be causing the blockages. Keyhole! So, they're going to make holes and put keys in there!

Turns out a laparoscopy is where they make tiny incisions in your skin and put a camera inside to get a good look for any issues and then fix them. Very clever. They also blow your tummy up with gas—as if I didn't have enough issues going on without extra farts being released during the day. Apparently, the reason behind it all is to get a better look inside at the reproductive organs. I was apprehensive, but also a bit excited at now FINALLY finding out the reason that would finally explain why I wasn't getting pregnant.

I'd also discovered a newfound love for anaesthesia. The moment before you go under you feel you've instantly had ten glasses of wine! What's not to love? I was nervous on the day going in and brought my home comforts like my pink fluffy dressing gown and slippers. Peter came and sat with me but wasn't allowed to wait. Luckily my name was called quickly.

I had to answer a zillion questions about my health, my drinking habits (like anyone really tells the truth!) My height was measured at 5ft1 (always a short arse; that's never going to change!) and my weight taken (no one likes that!). Luckily, I've always been fairly slim.

Next thing I remember is going in for my ten ~~glasses of wine~~, sorry anaesthesia, then waking up with a pain in my shoulder (from the gas apparently) and feeling very groggy! Now it felt like I'd had a massive night out with a terrible hangover. They told me the surgery went well and that the hospital would write to me with the results. Yay! Another eternity spent waiting! So I went home and slept for what felt like forever.

NINE
Infertile

*'Even the darkest night will end
and the sun will rise'*

Around a month later, like clockwork, the letter came. I was so anxious about opening it as this envelope contained my whole future. Taking a deep breath, I ripped it open and read the contents. I had a pelvic inflammatory disease. Back to the reason I told you about in chapter 1, my habit of choosing unsuitable partners who would cheat on me,. Protection wasn't used during these relationships and so there was fault on both sides.

I now found out that a chlamydia infection, which had gone undetected and untreated, had wreaked havoc on my reproductive system all those years ago. It had ravaged my tubes which had then caused my infertility. Although all tests showed I was now completely clear of infection—as STD testing was a part of the fertility testing—the damage had been done and was irreversible. It seemed one of my previous sexual partners had unwittingly caught chlamydia and then, symptomless, had passed it on to me. I, too, had been unaware of becoming infected, but the disease had lurked in my system causing untold damage and, on one occasion, would nearly end my life. You'll find out why as I'll explain later.

I was saddened but also relieved to have had a diagnosis of some kind so that I could begin to make plans of how I was going to continue my dream of being a mother despite the diagnosis. I was still hopeful I could one day make my dream a reality. Pelvic inflammatory disease is an infection of the reproductive system. The sooner it's caught then the sooner it can be treated with little long-lasting damage. Unfortunately, I didn't even know about pelvic inflammatory disease until I was diagnosed with it. It's known by doctors as the silent epidemic as symptoms often go unnoticed for years… until it's already done its worst.

If I can help just even one person through this book to avoid what I had to endure, it will be worth sharing my experiences. Seek help if you have any abdominal discomfort; get tested for STDs after each partner or in cases of cheating; see a medical professional if you notice any chances in discharge, menstrual cycle, bleeding and/or pain during or after sex (this didn't apply to me) or pain when urinating. Get checked out asap then I will be happy. These symptoms could also apply to other issues too, and you'll find out the further damage this deadly disease had on me.

I hadn't been aware at the time of the destruction it could cause, which had led to my infertility. Nonetheless, I was also grateful to have the opportunity to go through fertility testing and to have discovered this, otherwise it would have continued to create even more damage.

Looking back, I wish I had got myself checked out after the relationship or when I found out about the cheating. I was still so young, and my reproductive health definitely wasn't on my top list of priorities. Also, there wasn't the same openness and awareness around sexual health as there is now, so we were far less educated. Either way, I'm sure we'd all have things we'd do differently if we had the chance again.

Peter took the news hard and was really angry. Angry at my previous partner, but also angry at the situation which was affecting us now. We had an argument about it, and he went out for a walk to get some air. I felt completely helpless at this point because the issues we were having were down to me and there was nothing I could do to change that fact. It was just something we were both going to have to accept, live with and move on from. That's what we did; it wasn't really discussed again. We still had to combat the fertility issue we had on our hands, and arguing about a diagnosis that dated back over 15 years wasn't going to help matters.

The letter also explained that the doctor had managed to open up one of the tubes on the left side by making a hole through the other end and had tested it with dye again which seemed to be passing through slowly, but they'd just left the right-sided tube untreated. (God knows why they didn't just work on both or just remove both at that stage and refer me straight for IVF.)

They told me to go ahead and keep trying naturally now that the doctor had partially opened one up. I felt nervous and hopeful at the same time. I went online on to the forums to see if anyone else had been through a similar procedure, and as always there were mixed reviews, but it didn't seem to be an overly common issue. It was the best hope I'd had yet, so I was going to take the positive from it and continue trying. Peter and I decided to avoid putting more pressure on ourselves, and just wait to see what would happen.

TEN
My Nightmare Begins

*'Hardships often prepare ordinary
people for an extraordinary destiny'*

Life seemed to just pretty much continue as normal once
I'd had time to accept the pelvic inflammatory diagnosis.
Normal being trying not to overly obsess over anything
fertility or baby related, trying to stay off the forums because it had been getting to the point I would go and visit
family and friends and just scroll through TTC forums for
hours! Seriously not healthy. I had a mind once, before
all this began; I had a social life, and I used to have FUN!
Remember what that was?

So, I went back to going out with friends, trying
hard not to bore them with tears about my ongoing
struggles. I focused on work as I had a business to run,
artists to manage and I'd also set up a new business
licensing music, and was in the process of signing over
1000 songs to build my database of music to sell for
film/tv projects. Outside of the pursuit of fertility, I
had plenty on my plate to get stuck into, and it let me

feel half normal again. It was so easy to let the fertility struggles completely consume me as they already had many times before, and have them completely dominate my conversations, relationship, work and everything in between. Everything would suffer as a result, and so I was determined to focus on other things I had in my life.

Apparently, everybody knows and is told all the time that it's important to be relaxed, not to stress and pregnancy will happen! SHOOT ME NOW! If I ever hear that phrase again from people...anyone! Not sure about you but it's the number one, most irritating thing you can say to someone in the midst of a fertility struggle. The most dreaded question aside from 'Why are you still single/why aren't you married yet' to all unmarried members of the fertility club is, '*When are you two having kids? You need to get a move on you're not getting any younger.*' Yeah, well, you're not exactly a spring chicken, Susan!

You grit your teeth as you struggle to hold back the words 'mind your own f****ing business'. It's the one thing I'd never ask anybody as no-one knows what a person may be struggling with behind closed doors, even if they seem like they have a 'perfect Instagram life' on the exterior. Everyone is battling an issue of something, at some point. It's so important to be kind. Always.

Another suggestion I hate is, '*Give it time you're still young, you've got plenty of time.*' Oh, have I, Susan? And since when did you get psychic abilities so that you know what's in store for my future?

Or perhaps the dreaded '*Have you thought about adoption?*' This is just insulting: as if we've never thought of all the options available in the world to have a baby. In my case, I hadn't ruled it out as a last resort; or maybe once I'd had my kids, but I'd barely even reached my threshold of trying for my own and didn't need to be reminded of it possibly not working out by anybody, thank you very much. It's already an ongoing daily battle just to get past my diagnosis without needing any reminders from busybodies.

'*You're running out of time.*' Thanks, Ann, why don't you focus on your ducks and I'll focus on mine.

'*Don't worry—took me ages to get pregnant then bam it just happened when I wasn't even thinking about it.*' Whoop De Doo for you.

'*IVF worked the first time so it probably will for you too. Have you considered it?*' to the '*Oh we spent thousands on IVF, waste of money, just be prepared that you could go through all this and still be childless.*'

'*Have you tried* (insert many suggestions here that you hear). *My friend Lisa swears by it and she has three kids.*' Good for your friend Lisa and, no, I haven't and am not willing to try it, thank you!

I find that simply smiling through gritted teeth, trying to ignore the comments and carrying on with my day helps...who am I kidding? I normally call up my friend to have a massive bitching session and say, 'You'll never guess what that bitch of a woman, Susan, said to me...' which is what we women like to do...gossip and moan about it to whoever will listen.

Rant over, but I bet you can relate! Okay, back to all seriousness. After our letter of diagnosis and getting back to some kind of normality, I visited my friend, Joan. Joan has always been a really great sounding board, she's about fifteen years older than me and definitely lived a few trials and tribulations in this life so nothing fazes her. She had always helped me calm my mind when I'd been stressed or had a good laugh about things whilst cooking me up some delicious Caribbean food, which was her speciality and heritage!

We were sitting down at the table eating some of her amazing jerk chicken and rice one afternoon, putting the world to rights, when I noticed some bad shooting pains in my crotch area, so bad that I was wincing and barely able to sit down at all. My friend noticed this and said it wasn't normal.

I had been so used to pains from the pelvic inflammatory disease that I didn't think anything of it. But when Joan brought it up as a concern, and asked me how long it had been going on, I had a think and realised I had definitely been noticing a lot more regular random pains even when I wasn't having my period. I just assumed it was because I sometimes drank too many wines at a weekend. I'd also noticed that—(*if you're a bit squeamish—which most fertility warriors in this club are not—but just in case you can skip this next bit*)—that my period blood this cycle had been dark brown or pretty much a black colour, which I found odd. But again, I just passed it off as nothing. I'd lived with pains on and off for a long time and I had quite a high pain threshold, so nothing really set off an alarm inside me.

I promised Joan I'd make an appointment with the doctor and see what he said as, judging by the look on her face, it definitely didn't seem normal to her. Unfortunately, my medical practice had recently been classed as 'needing improvement' during a recent inspection so I didn't hold out much hope there. And just as I'd thought, when I went along to the doctors, my concerns were brushed aside.

I carried on as normal for a few more days and by this point, I was wincing when I went for a wee because it felt like the pressure from weeing was going to make something inside my lower abdomen explode. I went along to A&E and saw a doctor on duty a few days later. He couldn't figure out what it could be either and tested a urine sample I provided to see if it was perhaps a urinary tract infection (UTI). I explained that I'd just had my period and he said that, even though my period was a bit off-colour, it definitely ruled out pregnancy. Well, I had never been pregnant, so I highly doubted I could be pregnant too. He said my levels seemed a little off but not alarmingly, and so he gave me some antibiotics to go away with for a UTI.

It was coming up to Peter's birthday and I had a surprise rock climbing session with a private instructor to take us climbing outside at a well-known rock-climbing spot. It was to be a surprise as he had a lot more experience than I had at this! I was more of a horse rider, with a New Forest pony of my own rather than a rock climber, but I was always willing to try anything once.

It turned out to be quite fun, and I actually volunteered myself to climb up the rocks first. It was definitely tiring, but a good challenge. The instructor said I definitely had determination and perseverance as I refused to quit when I got stuck halfway climbing a huge wall. I thought, 'Climbing a huge rock that looks like it's halfway in the sky. That's nothing compared to climbing your way through a fertility jungle! That's where you truly learn determination and perseverance! Ask anyone that's been on this journey!'

It was a really great day and we enjoyed working together as a team, egging each other on to complete each challenge. I noticed while I was belaying that I was getting the random shooting pains through my crotch again which were making it very difficult to stand. I kept crouching down to relieve the pain. I brushed it aside at the time as I didn't want to ruin a great day and vowed to make another appointment with the doctor once I was home.

A few days later, I messaged the secretary of the consultant who did my laparoscopy and explained the symptoms I was suffering. I said I thought perhaps it was related to the surgery I had undergone because the pain was also one-sided and coming from the area which was operated on. The antibiotics I had been given for the urine infection hadn't made any difference and the pain was getting progressively worse and impossible to ignore.

It would come on intermittently during the day and I would have to hold my breath, while trying to deal with the shooting pains. I could barely sit down or go to the toilet without being in absolute agony. I thought perhaps it was scar tissue binding together as that can be quite common after surgery.

The secretary gave me an appointment and I went to the hospital, where I had the opportunity to explain the issues I had been having since the surgery. I explained the dark blood I had, which appeared almost black, and that the bleeding seemed a lot shorter than my normal period. I also mentioned the shooting pains, dull aches, and pain when going to the toilet.

I thought the consultant would be compassionate and be able to provide some relief and explanation for my symptoms, but she simply said, 'It's normal. All women have pain during periods. It's just something we have to deal with, I highly doubt it's from your surgery but if you still have the symptoms in another couple of weeks then perhaps make another appointment and we can look into it.'

I also said, 'What about the colour of the blood?' She responded, 'I wouldn't worry about it. Sometimes we can get old blood that comes through during a period. I also suggest that perhaps you may want to think about getting a move on with your fertility and perhaps think about going for IVF as you're nearly in your mid-thirties now and fertility declines with age.'

I was astounded. I couldn't believe someone—especially a healthcare professional—could be so heartless and show such a lack of empathy for the symptoms I was having and also for my fertility struggles too. Was I being overly dramatic? I wasn't one to make too much of a fuss, but I knew something didn't seem right. My instincts told me that something was off.

I walked out of there feeling completely deflated, helpless and now even more worried about my fertility issues than I had ever been. I couldn't even just go straight into having IVF because you have to follow a process with the NHS and show that you've exhausted all treatment first before they will even consider you for funding for IVF. Technically I still had my tubes, even if they weren't perhaps in fully working order so, on the NHS, I was deemed as being able to conceive naturally. My dream of holding my baby in my arms had never felt further from me.

I walked home, feeling completely sorry for myself, and sat on the sofa trying to process what had happened. No one was in so I was just sitting alone with my thoughts when I noticed a 'bang' against the back-door window. 'What a strange noise, quite loud too,' I thought. 'What an earth could it be?' I opened the back door and took a look. A helpless little bird, that looked quite young, had flown into the window and was going into a fit on the floor before it passed away. Poor little thing. As if the day couldn't get any worse, and how strange! It gave me a really weird, horrible feeling and I couldn't explain why.

I googled the meaning. Don't ask me why but I did. It read 'In ancient times when a bird flies into a window, it means that death is knocking at the door.' WHAT THE HELL! And it happened to be just when I was home alone. Great. I decided to wait for Peter to get home and to bury the bird, poor thing. I explained to him the disasters of the day and he told me not to worry, that we'd get to the bottom of whatever symptoms I was having. He told me not to worry about the bird as they fly into windows all the time. Really? I've never seen one!

ELEVEN
Pain Like I'd Never Known

'You never know how strong you are until being strong is the only choice you have'

We both went to bed early that evening, exhausted from the day and glad to be putting the day's events behind us. It was around 11 p.m. and I was just drifting off. Peter was already snoring away when I suddenly felt a severe pain searing through me like a red-hot branding iron pressing against me from the left side of my abdomen. It was getting stronger and stronger.

I woke Peter up as I had started getting breathless and urgently, through exasperated breaths, asked him to get the painkillers from downstairs. The pain was getting more and more severe, and I was getting beside myself, howling the house down, crying uncontrollably and terrified of what was happening to me. Peter quickly came back upstairs with the painkillers, but I knew they wouldn't have any effect on this type of pain.

Peter was beside himself with worry as he watched me lie there writhing around in bed, crying so hard I thought I'd lose my voice. He had rarely seen me cry so knew this was something serious. He kept asking over and over, 'What can I do, what can I do?' I replied helplessly in between sobs, 'I don't know what is happening to me.' I was absolutely terrified. He said, 'Do you think we need to get to the hospital?' I couldn't even take in what he was saying or respond.

I rushed to the bathroom, barely able to stand, putting my head over the toilet bowl and feeling as though I was going to throw up from the pain at any minute. Instead, I found myself lying on the floor of the bathroom hearing Peter urgently shouting something in the distance, hearing the panic in his voice. I didn't have the energy to stand, let alone respond. I felt like I was going to pass out at any minute and just wanted the pain to STOP!

I knew instinctively at that moment that I needed to get to the hospital as quickly as possible and needed to muster up all the strength I could to find some clothes to throw on somehow. I couldn't turn up in a nightie! I managed to stand with my legs feeling wobbly and throw some leggings on, while I said, 'We need to go to the hospital...now.' Luckily, the hospital was just up the road and about a two-minute drive.

Peter helped me walk down the stairs as I was taking the tiniest steps; anything more than that was too much. I was sweating profusely and struggling to catch my breath. I leaned against the garden fence outside whilst

Peter went to get the car. I tried to breathe slowly and deeply and stay as calm as I could. Peter helped walk me into A&E which felt like an eternity then we had to register at the front desk. I couldn't focus on speaking or remember what my name was. I must've looked as white as a sheet.

We were told to sit down and wait to be called, but I couldn't sit down. It was too painful. I rushed to the toilet a few times to try to be sick again. The pain was just overwhelming and nothing like anything I'd ever experienced in my whole life. I felt beyond dizzy and knew if they didn't get me soon, I would pass out. Fortunately, my name was called quickly and I went into a room and began explaining some of my symptoms and pain. But before I had a chance to go into it properly, I started vomiting everywhere. The nurse quickly grabbed me a bucket and I just couldn't stop.

She took me into a room with a bed where I could lie down. All I remember is struggling to be able to breathe. I could only take the tiniest breaths, but stayed surprisingly calm, despite not knowing what the hell was going on. I knew if I panicked, it would affect my breathing even further. Different nurses and people were coming in at different times to ask me questions which were mainly answered by Peter. Various blood tests and other kinds of tests were taken.

Hours passed by, but no one seemed to know what on earth was wrong with me. They did say though, they would be keeping me in the whole night to run more tests. It was around 3 a.m. and I was now gripping onto Peter with all my strength as waves of pain would come by every few minutes or so. It made me realise what contractions would probably feel like. I had the urge to sit up to breathe, as lying down, I felt almost waterlogged.

It was around 4 a.m. and I'd had nearly a whole night of putting up with the pain. Even though very strong painkillers were given to me, such as Oramorph, nothing stopped the intense burning pain I was feeling. The last test that was attempted was when a nurse asked me to wee into a plastic pot or something similar. I told her it was very painful for me to wee but I'd try. In the end, I did manage.

She went off with it then, came back around twenty minutes later and said, 'We ran a test, which was the last thing we thought to do and congratulations, you're pregnant. Did you know you were pregnant?' I said 'Um, excuse me! WHAT! PREGNANT! But I haven't been able to get pregnant!' I knew nothing about this, and I had had a period literally a few weeks ago so how was that possible? Peter was just as astounded as I was, but happy at the prospect at the same time. She explained I would be heading down for a scan in the morning and should try to get some rest. I couldn't rest, I was still in extreme pain and had just been delivered bombshell news.

Pregnant? I was excited by the thought that I had fallen pregnant naturally for the first time ever in my life. But I also knew this didn't feel right. Surely pregnancy wasn't painful like this? I had nothing to compare it to as I'd never been pregnant before, but something told me not to count my chickens yet. We were both exhausted from such a traumatic, eventful night. Peter was slumped in the corner of my room when the nurse came to get me around 7 a.m. in the morning. They told Peter to go home and get some rest as he wouldn't be able to come with me anyway and I had more tests and scans to be done. We both agreed that made sense and that he'd be kept updated once we knew more.

I was wheeled down into the scan area by my nurse and I had one hand on my tummy, feeling a connection to my first baby. There was a bit of a queue and another girl in a wheelchair was next to me waiting to be scanned as well, so I said hello and she explained why she was being scanned as there was an issue of not being able to see anything on the scan so she was having a second one done. I wished her luck as I was sent in to determine my fate.

The nurse explained she had to do a vaginal scan which involved inserting a probe inside me. WHAT? I'm already in pain. Are you serious? She had to, though, but it was excruciatingly painful as she needed to twist it to see around my uterus. I felt crushed when she explained she couldn't see an embryo or sac in there, but my pregnancy test had come back positive, so I was definitely pregnant. They just didn't know where it was. Great. I felt crushed. This didn't sound good at all. If it wasn't in the right place, then it didn't sound very hopeful that my baby is going to make it out alive.

They explained I'd need to have a second scan or something similar with the doctor (I don't remember) so I was wheeled to another scanning room where there were two ladies. The woman doing the scan was an Indian lady who seemed very direct and a 'tell you exactly how it is' kind of doctor, which I didn't mind as I needed to know the facts, although I was completely out of it by this point and in a state of shock, I think.

She inserted the probe, and again that was unbelievably painful. She apologised but explained that she'd need to keep it in there a little while. 'What has happened is that you are having an ectopic pregnancy, which has ruptured and you've lost a lot of blood. You've been very brave to have dealt with that and the pain. Because you've lost a lot of blood from the rupture of the ectopic, it's making it difficult to see anything as your abdomen is completely full of blood (which explains why I couldn't breathe and felt waterlogged!). We're going to get you into surgery asap as an emergency to remove the embryo. You'll need a blood transfusion so we need you to sign these forms to accept a blood donation. Basically, if you don't, you're going to die.'

An ectopic pregnancy is the leading cause of death in early pregnancy and affects 1 in 80 women. Symptoms may be: bleeding, shoulder tip pain, abdominal pain, bladder or bowel problems or collapse. Not all women have the same indicators either, so it's always best to get checked out if you're unsure about any symptoms you're experiencing, and it's always better to verge on the side of caution. It occurs when a woman's ovum (egg), which has been fertilised, implants (gets stuck) outside the womb. The most common place for an ectopic pregnancy is the fallopian tube but there are many other sites where an ectopic pregnancy can be located. It is, sadly, not possible to move an ectopic pregnancy into the womb to allow it to grow normally.

I was in complete and total shock now, but I finally knew what the extreme pain was and that I was right to get to the hospital when I did. I was wheeled into a ward with others and was told that the anaesthetists would be up shortly to get forms signed, etc.

Suddenly, I was sitting on the hospital bed aware that the lady opposite was constantly farting. I remember that clearly as it was one of the first things I mentioned when I started making phone calls, which made me giggle amidst the heartbreak. I was just trying to process everything I'd just been told and the fact I was about to head into surgery...again! And I was pregnant... But in an hour's time...I wouldn't be. It was just all too much to take in. First, I messaged Peter and said, 'It's an ectopic pregnancy, I'm going into surgery shortly to have the embryo removed.' I just couldn't face talking to him, it was too painful to even say out loud and I knew I'd just break down.

I have tears in my eyes now reliving this and sharing it with you, as it was such a painful, traumatic experience to go through. I rang my sister and explained to her what had happened, then just broke down in tears. She offered to drive down as she lived an hour away, but I told her not to worry as I'd probably be sleeping most the time anyway and I didn't think I was up to seeing anyone. I tried to lighten the situation by telling her about the farting woman opposite which was the one thing that actually made me laugh in the middle of such a dire situation.

The anaesthetists came up and went through all my details, etc., and before I knew it, I was being wheeled down on my bed into the theatre for the anaesthetic. I thought to myself I need to be strong now, I'm on my own but this is a time I need to step up and be brave. I also quietly said in my mind to my little baby, 'I'm sorry you didn't make it and that you tried, I will always love you, even if you were here for just a very short time.' I'm literally sobbing as I'm writing this; anyone who has been through loss would feel this and understand this pain. I found it a lot harder than the actual physical pain.

I felt so sad that my baby had tried to come through but had become stuck in my fallopian tube on the way. I also cursed myself and my body for not doing its job properly. I felt a whole wave of emotions yet felt numb at the same time. And all the while, I was still bleeding internally. The only solace I could take was the twenty glasses of wine (anaesthetic) and to be knocked out from this living nightmare for a while.

TWELVE
Recovery

'How very quietly you tiptoed into our world, silently, only a moment you stayed. But what an imprint your footprints have left upon our hearts'

I awoke from my surgery shivering uncontrollably. The nurse quickly put more blankets over me. The first thing I asked was if I had woken during my surgery as I had a sudden flashback of waking up on the operating table and seeing doctors standing around working on me, and hearing panic in their voices. Someone was saying, 'She's lost a lot of blood.' In my flashback, I sat up for a minute and could hear the beeping of the machines around me. Then, all of a sudden, I was pulled back down into my body again. It was very strange but felt real.

The nurse assured me there was no way I would have woken up. I can still remember the flashback as clear as day even now when I think about it. Very strange. I'll go into this a bit more a bit later in the book to explain that moment.

Before I could ask anything more, I was brought back to the here and now with searing pain from my abdomen and the nurse quickly gave me some fentanyl to help. I was given enough time to have a drink and attempt to eat a biscuit before I was wheeled into the ward. The memory of the previous night and the timeline of traumatic events which had occurred rang in my head, as my mind attempted to try to process everything that had happened in a hazy blur from the drugs and anaesthetic. I was so unbelievably exhausted, and sad I had to be woken up back to my nightmare.

I listened to the noises of the scurrying footsteps of nurses walking past the ward, trolleys being wheeled along and the murmuring from the patients around me, and just wanted to be anywhere but where I was. I didn't even want to be in my own skin at this point. I didn't have the energy to message anyone, so I just closed my eyes.

I must've fallen asleep because when I awoke, Peter was with me. He looked like he hadn't slept at all, and I could see the hard lines of worry on his face. He was trying to appear as normal and calm for me as possible. He had bought me a teddy as a present. I still have an image on my phone that he took of us at the time. I am asleep clutching the teddy and looking completely exhausted in every single way, as was Peter.

I always think it's important to have things to remind us of all events in our lives, the good, the bad and the ugly as those are what shape us. It was comforting to have him there as I had been through all the surgery and scans alone. We must have both fallen asleep because we were woken by the nurse who came to tell us it was time for visitors to go home. I knew I just needed to rest and sleep; it was all I could do at this point.

Suddenly I remembered that I had a video shoot happening the next day and it was now 8 p.m. I had a whole team of people who would be turning up to shoot the next day and I was in charge of overseeing everything. Just to make matters worse, it was for a brand-new artist I'd just signed too! I was never one to cancel things, but there was no way I could make it so I had to message them to say I was in the hospital and ask to postpone it.

It's always the way when life hits you full force with no warning: there's always something in the background that's been arranged that you hadn't even given a second thought to because your life has just been turned completely upside down. We always have worries in life—for me it's trying to juggle business, home life, family, friends, etc.—and we think it's the day to day that we need to constantly worry about and keep on top of.

I've spent so many wasted hours needlessly worrying about my artists' next release, if they've reached sales targets for their promotional campaign, or worrying because I haven't seen my friends in a while or picked up the phone to my mum/dad/nan/sister, etc., or constantly stressing about not being where I thought I would be in life, etc. But these aren't the real worries. They seem so small in comparison and, in a time of crisis, you wish you had those worries instead, rather than being blindsided on a typical weekday night by receiving some life-changing news or life being threatened in some way. Those are the real worries. The rest is just a waste of time that could be spent enjoying life.

I tried to get as much sleep as I could through the night but was woken every hour, it seemed like, to have my stats taken, blood pressure done and made to drink plenty of water. Before I knew it, morning had arrived, and I'd barely slept a wink from all the monitoring. I was hooked up to fluids so going to the bathroom was an interesting trip, dragging all the machinery into the toilet with me.

Walking was extremely difficult and painful, and I couldn't stand for very long without feeling exhausted. I was excited about having a cup of tea and breakfast, though. Nothing could keep me from my food and love of tea! The doctor came in to see me shortly after to tell me they had to remove my left Fallopian tube and the embryo.

She also explained that I had lost a lot of blood where the embryo had ruptured so a blood transfusion was required during surgery. She explained there was no way an ectopic pregnancy could be saved in any circumstances and emergency surgery is always required in the event of a ruptured ectopic, including removing the whole tube. The doctor was friendly and asked if I had any questions.

The only thing I could think of at the time was: had I any hope to be able to conceive in the future? She was positive about this and said I still had a remaining tube, so there was still hope as many women go on to have successful pregnancies with one tube, though there was always a risk of a second ectopic. I had already decided it was a risk worth taking.

The difficulty was also that I still wouldn't be considered for funding for IVF treatment through the NHS. With one remaining tube, I was still deemed as being able to conceive naturally despite the huge risk of the pregnancy getting stuck in my tube and threatening my life again. Whoever makes these rules seriously needs to rethink and reconsider them. Just because statistically I still had a tube, it didn't mean it was in working order. I could potentially put my life at risk again.

THIRTEEN
Coming Home

*'The one who left gentle footprints on
our hearts left a story worth telling'*

I was discharged from the hospital and told to recover at home. Peter came to pick me up. Walking out of the hospital took a LONG time as I could barely put one foot in front of the other without experiencing dizziness and extreme pain. They should seriously offer patients wheelchairs when having surgery like that. I was given morphine to take home to help with the pain. The journey home was really painful too, going over bumps and taking corners.

Emotionally, I felt as though I had been plunged into darkness. I felt completely empty and numb in every sense. I kept replaying in my head the events that had taken place, trying to make sense of it all. I didn't want to be around anyone, not even Peter. I just wanted to go upstairs to bed, curl up in a ball and sleep until the whole thing was completely over and I felt normal again. Sleep was my only escape at this point. Home didn't even feel like home to me. It felt like a strange, cold place, and everything in my life felt like that too. I climbed into bed and just slept and slept.

Peter would wake me at various times with food and drink or to bring me painkillers. The pain from the surgery was so intense it was difficult to block it out. A heavy feeling of complete sadness occupied the air within the house. My phone was beeping all day with messages, but I couldn't bring myself to speak to anyone, explain anything or talk about my feelings at this stage. I couldn't have talked about my feelings anyway even if someone had asked me. I was just empty and numb.

The next day, after waking, I heard a knock at the door which was strange as we weren't expecting anyone. It turned out to be my videographer from another one of my artist's video shoots I had had to cancel at the last minute. He hadn't received my message and was ready to go to the shoot. There I was, was standing there in my PJs, white as a sheet from the surgery, and trying to explain the situation. How embarrassing! Not that I cared at that point. Things definitely don't stop even if you've taken a hit by life at full speed.

A week literally passed by with me stuck in a cycle of sleeping and eating and taking painkillers. Very slowly I started to regain some strength to walk around and sit downstairs. I even managed to say the odd word to Peter. I realised that I had been so consumed with my own pain that I hadn't even asked him how he was. After all, we were both affected by that night and he had lived it too, all be it not physically.

I tried to watch some telly as I lay on the sofa but would just stare blankly into space for hours at a time.

'How did this even happen?'

'How did I miss a pregnancy?'

'Why did I not fight harder to be seen when I experienced the signs that something was wrong?'

'Why did I let myself get pushed aside when my instincts were telling me something wasn't right?'

'How am I ever going to recover from this?'

'I was pregnant for the first time maybe I can conceive naturally?'

'Maybe my other tube might be okay after all.'

'How am I ever going to be able to try again without panicking?'

I just felt really depressed and sad for my baby. People would tell me I was lucky to have got through this as it could've ended very differently and both the baby and I could have died. But I struggled to feel lucky.

I was still in complete shock, and my way of dealing with it was to shut myself off from absolutely everyone. Physically I was in agony as I hadn't been to the toilet for nearly a week because of all the meds and the shock to my system and trauma from the surgery, and when I was finally able to go it was incredibly painful. I had pain in the tip of my shoulder and burning pain at the surgical site on the left side of my abdomen which still felt like the ectopic, which then caused anxiety. My thoughts went in a vicious circle.

Peter and I started arguing as neither of us was communicating about the event or sharing how we felt about it. We were both quite similar in the way that we pushed everyone away and tried to deal with our emotions ourselves, a strategy which ends up pushing you apart. I felt like he hadn't truly felt what I had to go through as I was the one who had to experience the physical trauma. I felt, being a bystander in the situation, he wasn't showing enough compassion and would never understand what I really had to go through. But really, I knew it had affected him massively and he had experienced the loss too. On top of that, he had the worry of losing me as well. But it was difficult to see it from his point of view at that point.

One morning, after another argument, we both vented our feelings and I completely broke down in tears. It was the first time I had properly released any emotion. I admitted to the fact that I was struggling to deal with it all and move on. He also shared that, after leaving the hospital knowing about the surgery, he went home and rang his mum in floods of tears.

As the reality of the situation hit him, he felt utterly helpless, while also experiencing the loss of what would've been his first child too. He explained to me that he and his mum just cried down the phone. My family were desperately trying to find out what was happening the day of the surgery and were in constant contact with Peter; it was very distressing for all involved.

Peter's mum and dad came to visit a few days later as they wanted to give us support, and Peter's mum wanted to give me a hug, which was very sweet. I was still very pale, weak and disoriented. They brought us some flowers, and she wrapped me in her arms and gave me the biggest hug as we sobbed in each other's arms. Peter had tears in his eyes too, and his dad was also emotional. It was a very poignant moment, but very cathartic at the same time.

My mum was living abroad at the time and it was difficult to come back so it was nice to just feel a supportive hug and have a good cry. My dad and stepmum also came down shortly after, which was also nice, although I didn't have the energy to say much or to be with people for very long. It was nice to feel the support.

After I had recovered physically, the emotional scars still remained, and the trauma of the event still remains with me a few years later, to this day. I believe you never truly get over an event like that, you just learn to live with and be at peace with it. I really struggled to talk to any of my friends. I just didn't need pitying looks. They wouldn't make me feel better.

I know they were only trying to help and felt sad for me, but there was no one who could truly empathise or understand unless they had experienced it themselves. I really felt alone and terrified. I had one tube left and had to face the likely possibility of a future pregnancy with the risk of going through all the trauma again. So, was I prepared to roll the dice and take the risk?

Once I was physically strong enough, we went to the local church as we both really wanted to do something to remember the baby we lost. Peter wasn't particularly religious, but I believed in God and was very spiritual, and so we went to the church and lit a candle and said a prayer. It was difficult but it helped to release the emotion.

Thinking back, I probably should have gone through counselling to work through my feelings, but I always feel I can deal with things myself and soldier on, even when it's clear that it's not always the best way. Looking back now, I definitely had some form of PTSD from the trauma and would go on to suffer various flashbacks, which lessened as I got mentally stronger over time.

Peter went out one evening with some old friends he hadn't seen for a while and he called me while he was out saying, '*Bryony also experienced an ectopic pregnancy and went on to have two healthy children with her other tube. She says you should be fine as it doesn't mean the other tube was damaged.' I know he was only trying to help, but I didn't know if I liked my trauma being talked about, and it really wasn't what I needed to hear at the time. He was trying to lift my spirits and give me hope...and for himself, I think.

As I was healing, I passed away the time scrolling online and I came across the Ectopic Pregnancy Trust. This was a kind of saving grace for me in the midst of my turmoil. It was a charity dedicated to raising awareness of ectopic pregnancies, but not only that. There was a forum of lots of other women who had experienced similar ectopic experiences.

I began to read through lots of posts and felt I had finally found a place where others could truly feel my pain and offer words of hope and understanding. I posted my own story and received such lovely, helpful words from other women and from the trust itself, who I spoke to on the phone. I actually signed up a year or so later to assist the charity but had to stop for reasons I'll go into later. But giving back was definitely a huge part of my healing process once I was emotionally able to give and share.

To this day, I still go on to the forum and share my story with others to help them. I'm planning to assist again with the charity as it's important for me to be in a strong, clear-headed space in order to give help to others. I also recently received a personal message from a lady who was struggling with a recent second ectopic and was finding it hard to move past the dark place she was in.

She, too, was terrified for her future. She had one tube left so I gave her my email and we've been keeping in contact for the last six months as we update each other on our progress. She found it helpful with her healing to have someone to share her feelings with, someone who could understand and see that you could find peace again, which is another reason that prompted me to write this book. There just isn't enough awareness regarding ectopic pregnancies, yet it's the leading cause of death for early pregnancies. It goes misdiagnosed too often, putting mothers at risk.

Things took a turn for the worse in my personal life too; when it rains it pours! Shortly before the ectopic episode, my landlord found out I had been keeping a cat at the property I was renting (if you're struggling to have kids then you at least need a fur baby or two). I did ask for permission, but she had said no, and yes, I should've respected the rules, but it came at a time I needed something to look after, and my fur baby is still with me today.

A few days after coming out of the hospital the land-lady was pushing Peter and me to find somewhere to move out to (even though we had three months tenancy remaining). She began sending us images of houses to consider and it put too much pressure on us while I was trying to recover. In desperation, I tried explaining to her I had recently had surgery and needed to heal. She left it a week then started up again sending messages and pushing us to move. It was very stressful.

Luckily within two months we found a lovely prop-erty to rent in a beautiful part of the countryside near my horse, so it was perfect and had double the number of bedrooms for only £100 more than what we were paying on a grade 2 listed barn conversion with two rooms. We were also glad to be away from such a nasty landlord. It wasn't an easy process to move, though. We had to fight for our lost deposit back. The landlady, as it turned out, had a history of using threatening and bullying behaviour, taking whole deposits and threatening court action to those who stood up to her. We managed to sort it in the end, but it was an extremely stressful time. At least it took my mind off the ectopic incident!

An artist I had not long signed was also constantly calling me during my recovery to get his single released. I explained that things would need to be pushed back and gave the reason why. Despite this, I was still getting messages putting pressure on and pushing me to release it. There had also been other issues with this particular artist displaying showcasing diva type behaviour, and having experienced trauma like an ectopic, my tolerance level for others' behaviour wasn't—and isn't!— very high.

One day, I thought to myself, 'Why am I breaking myself for an artist that doesn't even care that I nearly lost my life and won't respect the need for my recovery?' I rang the artist shortly after I reached a decision and told him I would be releasing him from his contract and giving one month's notice. I was not in a place in life to add any extra stress and would definitely not be managing an artist who couldn't respect boundaries.

It felt good to let go. I'd sometimes felt debilitated when making a decision to let go of things, even when others couldn't understand why I was still holding on to things in my life that clearly weren't working. They were right! It was obviously a lesson I needed to learn, and my life has definitely been simpler since I cut things out like that. I just needed to learn to react quickly and trust my instincts!

FOURTEEN
New Home, New Start
(or so we thought!)

'Every end is a new beginning'

We got moved into our new home and it felt good to be making a new start, leaving behind the old memories in the last place. I really enjoyed being near my horse and being able to ride out in the woods behind our house a few times a week. It was really healing as I loved being out in nature and the outdoors. Christmas was slowly coming up too, so we had things to look forward to.

Our businesses were growing, and I'd had some extra money come in which enabled us to kit out our house with the extra furniture we needed now that we had more space to fill. We desperately wanted to buy our own place, so we were actively trying to put money away when we could to make it possible. It was difficult, though, when trying to build our businesses, which also can go against us with mortgage lenders, not to mention having to pay extortionate rents at the same time. I honestly don't know why the system can't be based upon your previous payments on rents to prove whether you can afford that amount, then you could afford a deposit. It's so backwards!

Even so, my wish to have children of my own was stronger than wanting my own home. Our cat, Lola, was allowed in this property which was a bonus! The area was really lovely, even if we were miles from the main town, but I've always been a country girl, so I didn't mind. It was Peter who struggled a bit being so far out, but we didn't have long to look and felt we were really blessed to find the property we did.

One of my artists was recording her EP in London with a producer, and normally I oversee the sessions and stay up there with the artist in a hotel and work nearby in case they need anything, and also to hear what they've created after each session. While in London, something didn't feel right this time, though. I kept having a feeling in my side that felt like a stitch that just wouldn't go away. It was a dull, nagging sensation and not a feeling that I particularly liked, as anything I feel at the sides of my abdominal area tends to freak me out, regardless. My mind starts to spiral and flashbacks of my ectopic start to appear again. This occurs even if there's zero chance in my mind that it's possible.

Something that day just told me to go and test for pregnancy, because previous experience told me to never ignore any symptoms and always check for pregnancy no matter what. Peter and I had been so busy with moving house, fighting battles with previous landlords and with our businesses that we hadn't actively been trying to conceive as I think we needed a bit of a break. I bought a test from the shop, went back to the hotel during the day while my artist was still recording, took the test and nervously waited. A few minutes later I nervously picked up the test to have a look. 'PREGNANT'. WHAT?!?!?! Seriously?

So I'd gone from spending years having every test saying 'negative', to now in the space of three months after my ectopic episode being pregnant—again. What the hell was going on? Had my reproductive system light just been turned on? I was absolutely shocked and astounded. I immediately rang my sister to see what to do as I was in the middle of London, on a work trip and now apparently pregnant—but with a possibility of it being ectopic again.

For some reason, the surgeon never attempted to open or fix this tube during my first surgery so I had no idea how it functioned or if it even could. My sister suggested I find the nearest hospital and get checked out as I didn't have a clue how far along I could be or what risk it posed at this stage. I rang Peter who was out with his friend and just spat it out, 'Peter, I'm pregnant!' I could hear him smiling over the phone, delighted by the news, but I quickly chimed in to remind him of the reality that the pregnancy could still be at risk given our history. He also advised me to get checked out.

I had a whole mixture of emotions. Luckily, after looking on my phone, I discovered that the hospital wasn't too far away. I thought I'd call an Uber to make sure I got there safely. An Uber turned up and took me a few metres up the road—literally! It would have taken me one minute to walk! That cost me a fiver! Okay, I clearly wasn't thinking straight.

Once there, I sat in the hospital waiting to be seen. There was quite a queue. Finally, I was seen, and my bloods were taken. They checked over my tummy as I complained of a dull, constant stitch but no bleeding. I explained my history, but the doctor said she couldn't feel anything abnormal. She also reminded me that lots of women go on to have healthy pregnancies after an ectopic. I tried to keep hold of that and not to get too nervous as I waited for the results of the hCG. For some reason, I always panicked when an hCG blood result came back (hCG blood results confirm pregnancy and the levels of pregnancy hormone to indicate how things are progressing).

I'd always worry that the test would go wrong and it would come back negative—although it never did. The doctor said the test was positive, but levels were low which meant the pregnancy was very early. Thank God! But I know now that the levels can also indicate whether the pregnancy is progressing well or if there might be a problem. All the while this was going on, my artist had been trying to reach me to listen to their session as they'd created a banger of a song. We also had an awesome writer from Switzerland co-writing in the session, who had written for some big names such as The Jacksons, and who was also a good friend of mine. How was I going to keep this to myself? Should I say something to them? Is it professional to share something as personal as this or should I keep it to myself? I was in complete turmoil, but decided to let them know I was at the hospital and would explain later over dinner.

I told them both that I was pregnant and that it was early days, but risky because of my previous history. You find that when you divulge this to people you'll always hear, 'I have a good feeling about this one.' But truly you never know how it's going to turn out. You prepare for the worst but hope for the best. They were both so excited about my news, but I was apprehensive.

I rang my mum and told her, and she was elated. That's the thing with pregnancies and fertility struggles, it's not just you or your partner that goes on this journey; all your family/friends and those around you, whom you decide to share it with, all go through it with you too. News got around fast and both Peter's family and mine were overjoyed. Perhaps finally this was our time.

The annoying thing about early pregnancy was that I had to wait until I was at least six weeks to be able to see anything at the scan as it needs to have developed enough by that point. Until then, I only had hCG blood tests to rely on to see if levels were climbing as they ought to, which generally indicates if things are progressing as they should.

The tricky thing with that is six weeks can be a time when an ectopic pregnancy can start rupturing, which as you know, can be deadly. Until I got those two lines on a test going for my six-week 'viability scan', I was on tenterhooks, worried for my life and the life of my baby. It's like walking a tightrope. Not very nice place to be at all. I couldn't think of anything else and my mind had a wonderfully annoying way of conjuring up all kinds of images and flashbacks to throw into the equation.

Finally, week six came around and Peter and I went into the Early Pregnancy Unit at the local hospital. I was a bag of nerves but prepared for any outcome (okay, I thought I was prepared). The nurse took us into a scanning room, got the probe and inserted it to have a look.

I don't remember much of what I was told at that time. We sat nervously in another room as they said they needed to check the results of the scan, waiting to hear the verdict that would perhaps be a joyous occasion or absolute torture that would flip our lives upside down again. The only positive I could take from it was that I could be more prepared this time knowing the facts rather than have everything rushing at me at a million miles per hour. Peter and I discussed how we would handle each outcome regardless of how it would turn out. I tried to convince myself I had it together. I would cope no matter what and there were still options to achieve my dream.

The nurse came back in, and she didn't need to say anything. I instinctively knew the answer before she opened her mouth. 'I'm really sorry to have to tell you this, but it's looking like the pregnancy is within your right fallopian tube so it is ectopic. We've checked the hCG levels and they are too high to offer you Methotrexate.' (Methotrexate is a drug they give you to terminate the pregnancy and stop the pregnancy from developing further to prevent rupturing. This is effective in the early stages.)

She explained I would need surgery and that they had a bed available later today if I wanted to go home to pack and come back later. Almost as if I was booking a hotel room. If only it had been. She left the room to give us some space. I burst out crying, hugging Peter in disbelief that we were having to go through this yet again. 'How could life be so cruel?'

We were devastated, although Peter felt he had to keep his emotions in check to be strong for me, which is a typical reaction for a lot of guys. I was numb, shocked but trying to keep it together. We went back home in silence, and I began to pack my things up. I thought to myself 'great timing'. It was only a matter of weeks before Christmas Day. It wasn't just the surgery I had to quickly prepare for—it was also the recovery time I had to factor in. I think, putting my focus on the physical attributes, I was protected from the real pain of losing another baby. That was just too painful to even consider at this stage.

It took a while to find a parking space when coming back to the hospital later (Peter got a ticket too) and by this point, I was really starting to feel dizzy. I was holding onto the side of the wall on the way and needed to stop every few steps. The symptoms were starting to kick in and I was panicking about it rupturing and having to deal with the extreme pain (some women on the forums comparing this as being worse than child-birth). Peter reminded me I was in the best place and being monitored so I should try not to panic.

I had a lot of blood tests done with the thickest needles I'd ever seen which left horrible bruises covering my whole hand. The doctor then came in to insert the catheter as the nurse was struggling and got blood everywhere. I thought 'Jeez I hope my surgery goes better than this! I'm putting my life in their hands!' The doctors were very sympathetic towards me, however, and recognised me from the first time around. I was clearly becoming a regular. They explained I'd be going into the theatre later that day, and fortunately I hadn't eaten/drunk since the first thing in the morning.

Peter was told to go home and, once again, I was left to face this on my own. I knew I had to be brave. If I could just focus on the small positives, such as the an-aesthetic I'd come to 'enjoy': all those strong drugs that made me feel out of it! I even enjoyed the endless cups of tea once I was allowed them. These things would help me through—anything to take away the fact that this was my third surgery in one year, two surgeries in the space of three months and second pregnancy loss in the space of three months.

My poor body, what had I put it through? They wheeled me into the anaesthetic room and the anaesthetists all wanted to discuss my career choice once they learned what I did for a living. I think they like to keep you talking to keep your mind off the fact you're going into surgery. Then, all of a sudden, 'Hello wooziness, my old friend.'

I awoke from the surgery in the recovery room, again asking the doctor if the surgery had even gone ahead as I was very groggy and didn't know what was happening. She said it had, then the familiar pain started so she gave me some fentanyl which helped and some water. I asked about a cup of tea, which she said would come later. After I was a bit more with it, I was wheeled into a room on my own this time, which I was really happy about as I certainly needed privacy.

Peter and I sent messages back and forth as he was checking in on me and explaining that his family and mine were checking for updates. I have to admit I was pretty out of it. I'd had my limit of painkillers too, which was annoying. Eventually, I tried to get a bit of sleep until the hustle and bustle of clattering and nurses walking around and beeps going off woke me up around 6 a.m. I had some breakfast—well, tried to eat what I could before the consultant who did my surgery explained that they removed the embryo which had slowly started to rupture as there was a bit of internal bleeding, so thank God I had surgery when I did.

He also explained that the tube was beyond repair and he had needed to remove it in order to ensure my safety. He went on to tell me that this meant both my tubes were now removed which meant I was deemed clinically infertile. I would no longer be able to conceive naturally and IVF would be my only option to conceive in future. This was a difficult pill to swallow. Not only did I need to mourn for this baby I had just lost, but I also needed to mourn my fertility. He stated that many women still go on to have children through IVF and that having the tubes removed actually helps to assist the IVF process and limits chances of ectopic pregnancy. It was so much to take in.

Infertile? I wasn't even in my mid-thirties yet. I felt numb, shocked and sad. I was just trying to cling onto a glimmer of hope which I'd never completely lost even in the darkest of times. There were still options. It didn't have to end here. I think by this point I was in denial about my loss and trying to put on a brave face to the world and convince myself I was okay. I simply had to get on with things as normal and keep powering on through fertility treatment. I hadn't even allowed time or space to truly mourn the loss of another baby. I think it was my mind's way of coping, but really, I was in denial. The nurse at the hospital said she would now refer me for fertility treatment on the NHS as there was nothing more they could do for me now that I was infertile. I was finally eligible to potentially receive funding from the NHS for IVF.

FIFTEEN
Recovering from Loss

'Learn to see the gift in adversity. By doing this you will begin to find true peace in your struggle'

In the days after being sent home from the hospital, I tried to recover as much as I could. No-one knew what to say to me, now that it had happened again. After I had recovered from the physical pain, the emotional pain started to show itself.

Deep down, I felt so lost and guilty that I couldn't protect my babies, even though I knew there was nothing I could have done. I went back onto the ectopic forum and posted about my second experience, and said that each time this tragedy happened it seemed to take a piece of me with it.

Someone responded, explaining that they too had experienced two ectopics resulting in two surgeries in a row. It was comforting to know I wasn't alone in this. The hospital invited us to a Memorial Day where we could remember all the babies that were lost and they'd scatter the ashes together in their special garden, but neither of us wanted to go. I also chose to try to not remember any birth dates either. I know many do and it helps. I just personally chose not to as I wanted to honour my babies but then try to put it behind me. I didn't want to remain 'stuck'.

We went back to the church and lit another candle and I wrote out a request for prayer. Peter's mum said she couldn't understand why it kept happening to us, why God could be so unfair. I was of the belief that perhaps it was a lesson of some kind for me to learn, even though I didn't know why at this stage. I always liked to think there was a reason behind everything, even if we weren't consciously aware of it. I pushed any emotion right down inside and locked it securely away, and continued to be in denial.

Christmas was around the corner and we had previously offered to host it at our new house this year. I didn't want to cancel plans at the last minute, and I thought it would be a good distraction, so we went about getting the last bits we needed. I recovered physically quicker this time too, and we put all our focus into Christmas plans and organisation. We were bringing together both families for the first time and I had never cooked a Christmas meal before. For seven people!

We were glad to get caught up in the hustle and bustle of it all and it was nice to be around family during this time and to have the support and their happy energy around. We managed to push our feelings aside as I was determined not to have it ruin my Christmas. I'd already spent months in a depressive state, feeling helpless, and I just wanted to try to put everything behind me as quickly as I could and move on.

We had a great time, and it was nice to be able to live life again. It was also nice to take some time off of work and focus on piecing myself back together, which was really important as we now needed the energy to start a whole new journey—IVF. Many people around me told me to wait as:

A. I needed to let my body heal
   after three surgeries

   and

B. I needed to be in an emotionally strong place to be able to deal with
   the emotional roller-coaster of IVF

Looking back, they were completely right, but I'm a pretty stubborn person and this was my way of coping—throwing myself back into it all and keeping on trying. I felt helpless if I wasn't taking action of some sort. Peter was happy to go along with whatever I chose to do as it was my body that would have to go through it. I literally had no idea of what we were letting ourselves in for! Nothing can warn or prepare you!

SIXTEEN
IVF 'Expect the Unexpected'

'Retrieve, Believe, Conceive'

We waited the obligatory three months for our first consultation to come through the post confirming our appointment. Then we had to wait another few months after that to actually go for our first IVF appointment. We were used to waiting by this point, but it didn't make it any easier.

We were excited that we were making progress and finally able to receive treatment. We truly believed IVF was made for people with no fallopian tubes and actually helped increase success rates and lower ectopic risk, which gave me a lot of hope. We went into it completely blind and full of confidence and belief. This was the answer to all our problems, especially since the original problem of my tubes had now been removed.

I was once again positive about the future and holding on to the hope that it would all work out for us with this magical treatment. Thank the Lord for whoever created this fabulous invention. The day of our appointment arrived. We scrambled to find our way through what felt like a maze, and walked through a tunnel of ghosts to get there (a creepy walkway which was a tunnel that linked the fertility centre away from the rest of the hospital. It was dark, dingy and definitely not a place you wanted to walk through alone at night).

We finally found the right place, gave our name to reception and sat down in the waiting room full of other fertility warriors waiting to be seen. All of a sudden, we heard our names being called which we responded to, then a lady who must've been the receptionist's assistant said in a loud, booming voice in front of everyone, 'You're not supposed to be in here, you're meant to be in the infertility clinic which is down the hall.' In front of everyone in the waiting room! We were MORTIFIED!

Okay, it was obvious we all had an issue with fertility as we wouldn't have been sitting there otherwise. But to have it spelt out in front of others was something else. We quickly scampered and found the 'infertility section' down the hall. So we weren't even at the stage of seeing the fertility centre for treatment, sigh. What another let-down after so much waiting again! We patiently waited for our name to be called and an Indian lady came out and ushered us into her office to discuss our referral. She asked me questions about my history which I found difficult to go through again, and Peter's too, then went on to explain the criteria for funding from the NHS, which is very strict. It's also very unfair as what you're entitled to is dependent on your postcode. In some areas, you're allowed up to three full rounds and in other areas none at all. For our area, we were potentially entitled to one full round which includes one fresh cycle and one frozen cycle.

The criteria are as follows: up to forty-two years of age, be in a relationship for more than three years with your partner, Body Mass Index within the range of 19 to under 30 kg/m2 and males under 30kg/m2 for a minimum of six months. No previous kids are allowed including adoption from both sides.

So, if your partner had kids from a previous relationship and you'd never had kids, you would still be excluded from funding even though the kids are from his ex-partner which I find very unfair. Luckily that didn't apply to us. You have to be non-smokers, both of you for a minimum of six months, which is fair. If you've had recurrent miscarriages, you'll be directed for treatment but not offered IVF as you can conceive naturally, which again I believe isn't fair. Same-sex couples need at least six failed attempts of donor insemination before being offered treatment.

We were told our next appointment would be at the fertility centre (the one we'd just tried to access) and we would be undergoing tests to determine our eligibility for funding. We decided to make sure that we overhauled our lifestyles again and I made sure I was keeping fit. We ate fairly healthy anyway, but I cut out all wine and chocolate snacks that I had on a daily basis—okay, well… I limited them. I always gave my all for anything important that was needing to be prepared for. Everything else I avoided, apart from chocolate. You need some treats on this hard slog.

Workwise, I had a lot going on as my artist was due to film a couple of live covers in a multi-million-pound recording studio, which we were excited about. I had final plans to sort out with the engineers who were recording it and with the videographers who were going to be filming it, along with a photoshoot for the artwork which was going to be used alongside the releases.

I also had another artist gearing up to release her second single and had a video shoot planned for that which also needed a lot of arranging and scheduling. On the licensing side of things, in my other business, which involved signing lots of new music and finding opportunities in film/tv to match the songs to, I was making some headway and starting to get some placements for our artists and writers in some notable TV series and films after years of blood, sweat and tears alongside all the fertility struggles.

I had attended quite a few conferences in major cities in the US and London on my own, while trying to make as many contacts as I could as I was completely new to this side of the industry. When I started out, I had zero experience and knew nothing about the legal side of music and copyrights. I'd had to find my way in the dark and fumble along for a few years until I picked things up, so I was very happy that I was landing deals. In my first one, however— because I didn't know what I was doing—I lost out on a $12k deal and was cut out completely because of a silly mistake, which I've never made since. But overall, things seemed like they were looking up in all areas. It's rare in life to have all areas synced up and going well at the same time.

Our appointment came around and I felt a bit nervous about all the testing we had to do. While sitting in the waiting room, we played a guessing game, trying to work out what other couples' issues were and why they were here. The people waiting to be seen ranged from fairly young couples to couples in their forties. It amused me how the waiting rooms were like a library.

Nobody dared speak or even look at each other, which seemed crazy as it was literally the Secret Fertility Club, and we were all in this together. The best thing would have been to share our stories with one another. It didn't need to be a secret. Yet we all anxiously avoided one another and didn't make eye contact. It would have been so much nicer if we had all confided in one another. Maybe it's a British thing. We're always quite reserved.

We were eventually called in by the nurse and had to sign a zillion forms, with one giving me permission to use the embryos if anything happened to Peter—a horrible thought. Another focused on what would happen if we split up as a couple—what would happen to the embryos? (You can donate them or offer for them to be used for educational purposes for the science lab, etc.) We then had our weight and height taken along with a carbon monoxide test to ensure we hadn't been smoking.

We passed all the tests with flying colours and were told we'd be receiving funding and would be able to start treatment. We were ecstatic and felt like we were finally on our way to our dreams of holding our child in our arms. We knew the statistics of IVF, but every case was different and I was going to go into this with a positive state of mind and nothing else. I was going to give it my all.

To get ourselves in a positive frame of mind, and to give ourselves a break before starting our treatment, we decided to go on a holiday to Venice. We deserved it after all we'd been through, and we realised that there probably wouldn't be another chance after I got pregnant. We decided on Venice for our first trip abroad together as it is such a beautiful, romantic city.

Venice certainly lived up to its promise. Although we stayed on the outskirts, in Lido, we hugely enjoyed taking the water taxi into the city and promised ourselves we would get the speedboat second time around. The cobbled streets were a draw, and we wandered aimlessly for hours, loving the richness of the atmosphere and the wonderful little shops, not to mention gorging on authentic Italian cuisine—my favourite! We also visited the islands of Murano, Burano and Torcello. The exquisite glass-blowing was incredible.

We hired a guide to take us to the best places to eat and drink which was a lot of fun—until he took us to a sandwich shop selling horse meat! And me with a horse I loved! A night at the opera was amazing (even though I couldn't understand a word).

To finish off, we went on a trip to the Prosecco Hills. There were vending machines selling bottles of Prosecco at really cheap prices along with miles of beautiful vineyards all around. We went to visit a couple of the vineyards for Prosecco tasting, and ended up getting a bit tipsy, to say the least (so much for my health kick). We even bought a couple of bottles to take home which I wouldn't be able to drink as I was going to be pregnant soon.

After Venice, we met up with Peter's mum and sister in Gibraltar to celebrate their birthdays. We had such a laugh and my last few glasses of wine before I'd have to stop anything naughty crossing my lips for a long time.

SEVENTEEN
Starting The Meds

*'You were given this life because
you're strong enough to live it'*

Our last appointment before we started the actual treatment was to go through the schedule—and it was a packed schedule even by my standards, and I managed the diaries of a couple of artists and two businesses. I knew I'd have to sit down, once home, to go through it all in stages and pin it to my wall and set up numerous alarms on my phone.

The medication protocol was as follows:

❖ Buserelin—daily injections to switch off
   hormones and reproductive system

❖ Scan—to check ovaries are quiet

❖ Gonal F—to mature and grow
   eggs to boost normal supply

❖ Ovitrelle Trigger Injection—
  to trigger ovulation

❖ Scan—to monitor and check eggs are
  growing nicely, ready for harvesting!

❖ Egg Collection—A short surgical procedure to harvest the eggs

❖ Peter to do his ahem business
  by ejaculating into a cup

❖ On same day mix the egg
  and sperm together

❖ Wait for embryos to form

❖ Receive a call from the clinic to tell you
  how many embryos formed and the quality

❖ Embryo Transfer Day!

It seemed fairly straightforward, but there were many, many things that could go wrong during an IVF cycle, which isn't always explained at the beginning either. There are also many different forms of IVF: you can have a medicated and a natural cycle (not on the NHS; it's pretty standard protocol). We were shown how to do the injections into your tummy and had to practise on a bit of rubber using water in the needle!

We were to start with the Buserelin injections to switch off the reproductive system to stop the eggs growing. This was to enable the cycle to be manipulated and timed with precision. The Buserelin basically put my body into mini-menopause, so I experienced things like hot flushes and mood swings. My body dried up completely so I could forget about sex, not that I felt like it anyway as I felt terrible.

Headaches occur like a constant hangover without any of the good side. Weight gain happens, especially around my middle so that I looked nine months pregnant before I'd even begun! Tiredness, dizziness, the list is endless! Everyone reacts differently, though; some don't get any side-effects. I suffered pretty much all of these.

The minute I first took the drug, I could feel it coursing around my whole body and my heart was beating so fast. Then I had to take a second daily injection a few weeks later to boost the follicles to grow more eggs. I felt like a voodoo doll! I had plenty of scans to check the progress of things, and I felt VERY bloated. Just before egg collection, I felt as though I was carrying heavy grapes around. My abdomen felt very tender to touch. We had a final injection to mature the eggs then they were ready to harvest.

Egg collection was quick too, well, not that I know as I was unconscious. But apparently, it was only thirty minutes if that. I felt a bit anxious coming off the anaesthetic, as though I had stayed up all night in my teens taking things I shouldn't have. During an egg collection, they basically passed a long needle (gulp) through my vagina to collect the eggs. They then mixed this with Peter's sperm after he'd done his difficult bit—Hahaha! Then, as with all things in IVF we had to wait to see if the eggs and sperm fertilise to become embryos, which takes approximately 16–20 hours.

Sometimes the sperm is injected directly into the egg (ICSI) although we didn't have that. We then had to wait for a call from the clinic to tell us how many had successfully fertilised and how many didn't make it. It's an agonising wait to hear. As usual. Sounds like a simple, straightforward process but so much can go wrong during this stage. It's mother nature mixed with science here!

IVF is extraordinarily clever and the guys who invented it, Patrick Steptoe and Robert Edwards, back in the 1970s, are literally geniuses. They've transformed so many lives and created so many new ones. It's incredible! However, I want to list some of the things that can go wrong here, not to scare anyone about to embark on this journey but to make sure you're going in with your eyes open:

❖ No embryos get fertilised. Luckily, we've
   never endured this, but many have. It
   must be heart-breaking. To think of all
   the effort and drugs that were taken
   and still things didn't go to plan. Even
   worse, the process has to start all over
   again. Very frustrating I'm sure.

❖ Partner feels too much pressure or, for
   some reason, fails to rise to the occasion
   (mind the pun here). The eggs have been
   taken but there are no sperm to fertilise
   them so the eggs are useless. (I think there
   may be back up plans for this beforehand)

❖ There are no eggs to harvest or the
   quality of eggs isn't good enough
   to continue (this is heart-breaking,
   but there are options I believe)

❖ Ovarian hyperstimulation syndrome
   (OHSS). Most symptoms of OHSS (nausea,
   bloating, ovarian discomfort) are mild.
   They usually go away without treatment
   within a few days after the egg collection.
   In severe cases, OHSS can cause large
   amounts of fluid to build up in the abdomen (belly) and lungs. This can cause very
   enlarged ovaries, dehydration, trouble

breathing, and severe abdominal pain. Very rarely (in less than 1% of women having egg retrieval for IVF), OHSS can lead to blood clots and kidney failure. This is rare, but it's good to be aware.

❖ Eggs could be released at the wrong time which then can't be retrieved for harvesting during egg collection if the trigger shot to release them is not done with precision (clinics do this all day every day, so it is quite rare).

❖ If either partner gets ill during treatment (this would be really unfortunate, but the treatment would then need to be delayed/cancelled).

There are other things that can go awry, but I have listed quite a few. For the ones whose cycles don't go to plan, there are many that do go on to be successful, even if it takes a few goes as IVF is also a numbers game. The statistics aren't really high for success, so you have to keep rolling the dice to succeed. This comes at a cost, though, so it is down to both partners to want to keep trying, ensuring that they are on the same page throughout and having the funds available and the emotional capacity to keep going.

We were lucky in our cycle as I responded well to treatment and we had four high-quality day five blastocysts. This is the pinnacle to aim for, typically. Some people have embryos transferred on day three. It's also very subjective as 'poor quality' embryos transferred at day three have still seen successful pregnancies whereas top-quality day five blastocysts, like ours, have not.

The grading also doesn't tell you what is going on inside the embryos genetically. This can have a major impact on the results because, if the body detects an issue with the embryo, then it's highly likely it will then detect that there is a genetic issue and will want to 'dispel the embryo'. Further development of the embryo will cease and a miscarriage is likely.

Sorry to be black and white as so much emotion is tied into this and it's heart-breaking when it happens, but in scientific terms, this is what is happening the majority of the time. Day three embryos are referred to as 'cleavage stage' embryos. The reason for this designation is that the cells in the embryo are dividing (or cleaving) but the embryo itself is not growing in size (Ref: Arc fertility).

Day five: a healthy embryo will form a blastocyst by dividing its cells into sections that will form the foetal matter and placenta. Depending on how well these different parts are formed, it can be graded from 'A' to 'D'. Unless it is a 'D' grade, the embryo can then be replaced in the uterus (Ref: Simply-Fertility).

Peter and I did everything by the book and were full of excitement and enthusiasm for the whole thing. We were complete newbies. I had read a few books and listened to podcasts on what to expect, but nothing can actually prepare you for the process. Everything seemed to be going swimmingly; our scans were all positive and my body was responding well. Our embryos were top grade, so we had everything on our side.

At the time, I thought my previous issues had been sorted when my tubes were removed. As they had caused the problem, nothing was now standing in the way and IVF was the perfect solution. The nurses seemed really positive about the outcome too.

Everything was on our side, which made the meds and constant poking and scans and probing easier. We had four top-quality day five blastocysts and nine in total, but five didn't make the distance, so we ended up with four top-quality embryos. That's okay, I thought, as we only need one to make it. The doctors explained that they would only transfer one and we had our date for transfer. We were nervous but so happy that all our hard work was going to pay off and we'd finally get everything we'd hoped for.

I'd been having acupuncture as I was doing everything I could to make things work this time and had heard that acupuncture was effective in helping implantation rates. It definitely made me feel relaxed, anyway. I also watched many videos on tips for implantation and read as many websites as I could in case there was something I'd missed. I wanted it to be perfect and was willing to do anything I could do to help Mother Nature along.

My acupuncturist told me to wear thick socks and gloves on the day of transfer so no heat would escape and to only consume warm foods and drinks, to keep my tummy and back warm at all times, and no stress. She clearly hadn't done IVF, then!

EIGHTEEN
Day Of Transfer

'Let your faith be bigger than your fear'

On the day of the transfer, we left super early to arrive as we needed to avoid any stress at all costs. We arrived and waited until the embryologists sat down with us prior to the transfer to talk through the procedure and wish us luck. They explained they'd be freezing three embryos and transferring one. I was certain, that between all four, we'd have a successful pregnancy. There was no doubt in my mind whatsoever.

I was bursting for the toilet as you must have a full bladder with the transfer. We waited again to be called into the room where they'd be doing the transfer and I removed my bottom clothing and wrapped myself in a paper towel. Oh, the luxuries! I was nervous by this point, not knowing what to expect. There was a nurse and doctor in the room with me and there was a little hatch in the wall which was open. They explained the embryologist would be passing the embryo through the hatch ready to be transferred into my womb.

They had a small screen they were using to pinpoint where in the womb to transfer the embryo. Peter, who was sitting next to me, watched the process on a huge TV monitor in front of us so we could watch the process of our baby being conceived together. It was such a magical but scientific process.

I thought, not many people get to see exactly when their child is conceived. I was told to lie back, put my feet in stirrups (gulp) and to relax. RELAX! My feet are in stirrups! I then caught a glimpse of the catheter they were going to insert through my vagina, and it seemed as long as a garden hose. Now I was nervous. I felt very uncomfortable, but I reminded myself it was a small price to pay.

They pinpointed where they were going to insert the embryo into the womb which they would pass through the inserted catheter. The embryologist, who was a male in his fifties or so, began the procedure by passing the embryo along the catheter to the female doctor, doing the transfer via the open hatch, and proceeded to inject the embryo into my womb. And just like that, in a split second, it was there, and I was PUPO (pregnant until proven otherwise). It was tiny, but they took a small picture (screenshot) of the scan for us to take away, like a souvenir of the day. Peter was elated and filming the whole thing. I was excited but needed to pee.

After transfer, I tried to take things easy and continued to work. I had an artist a few days after the procedure shooting a video in a luxurious multi-million-pound house that required a lot of extras and another artist releasing hers not long after so there wasn't too much time to rest.

I was thankful for it, though, as the dreaded 2WW (two-week wait) was almost too much to bear. I had so many thoughts running through my mind...will this/won't this work? I checked every little symptom and googled 'pregnancy symptoms'. I definitely felt as though something had burrowed itself into my womb as it felt so noticeable, but I didn't want to count my chickens too early. We also felt comforted by the fact that we still had embryos stored and one last round on the NHS for a FET (frozen transfer) if it didn't work out, but we were hopeful it would. Everything had gone so well for us and responded so well to the meds, etc., but we also were aware of the statistics.

Ten days soon passed and although the clinic advised not to test early in case of a false result from testing too soon, we couldn't wait any longer and I took a pregnancy test at home. I was beyond nervous waiting for the test to work its magic and kept telling myself, 'If it's negative, we can always try again and we're incredibly lucky that we have another round that's funded.' I anxiously waited, my heart racing while I sat in the bathroom counting the minutes...I picked it up...PREGNANT!!! Oh my God! I double-checked the packet instructions to ensure I'd read it correctly then rushed into the bedroom as it was the first thing in the morning and told Peter the good news. We were over the moon, beyond excited. Finally, our rainbow baby was here and all our hard work had paid off. Nothing could bring us down from the cloud of happiness we were bouncing on.

Telling friends and family was such an incredible moment as they'd been on the journey with us and this baby felt like he/she belonged to us all. I just hoped that the blood test also came back positive as I always worried it was just in my head or the test had been wrong. But a few days later, the blood test also came back positive too and the clinic congratulated us. We had officially graduated. We were now passed over to the Early Pregnancy Unit at the local hospital as I was still considered 'high risk' due to my previous ectopics. Now it was a case of just waiting for the first scan. I wasn't worried, I had no concerns as nothing could bring me down from this high.

I woke up every day in a state of excitement. I immediately stopped riding my horse and arranged for him to be looked after in his day-to-day care. Workwise, I was also in the middle of arranging a busy tour as my artists were both due to be touring southern UK within a few months and it was their first tour so I knew I needed to be there. I had no idea at this stage how I was going to make it: work travelling around the country and going to Wales while pregnant. Peter was concerned about my schedule too, but I figured I'd find a way to make it all work.

Our first scan soon rolled around, and we were super excited to see how our little one was developing. I decided to book a private scan not far from where we lived and could barely sleep the night before from being so excited. I was also apprehensive and nervous but tried to stay positive. When we arrived at the scanning centre, it was fairly busy with couples waiting their turn to be seen.

All of a sudden, I started getting horrific pains on one side of my abdomen. I felt almost as though I was going through another ectopic episode again. My heart was beating so fast, I felt my temperature rise and a searing pain running through my abdomen. It was so unbearable I couldn't focus on anything else but didn't want to make a scene either, so I started walking around outside in the car park to see if it would dissipate. Peter didn't know what to do and felt very concerned.

I figured we were in the best place as they would be able to see if anything was wrong. I just wanted to know what it was. We were soon called for our turn and the nurse and sonographer both introduced themselves and asked me to change and wrap myself in a paper towel. I quickly explained to them I was not only nervous but in a lot of pain too and they reassured me they would be hopefully able to see on the scan what the problem might be.

They inserted the probe and were quick to reassure me they could not only see the embryo but a heartbeat too. Peter and I were both elated. We could see the little flicker of a tiny heartbeat pumping away at a million miles per hour. I let out a huge breath from the tension and stress I was carrying and started crying (which was rare for me). I was so shocked that everything was coming together and my dream of having a baby was finally being realised. Peter had tears in his eyes too. We'd already experienced so much to get here and it was such a special moment after receiving so much bad news.

The sonographer said she couldn't find any particular problem but did see that a cyst had burst on one of my ovaries, so perhaps the pain could've been due to that. I wondered if a cyst had been caused from the meds to boost my eggs as I was so sick after that. I would never find out. We waited on the sofa for our pictures to be printed out then went back home with them, on top of the world!

NINETEEN
Not Everything Is As It Seems

*'Not in the absence of fear, of despair,
but the strength to conquer them'*

The first single from my new artist had gone through the roof. With the PR campaign behind it, it was reaching hundreds of thousands of streams, which was great news. We'd finalised details of the tour for both artists and they would be covering different cities and somehow I needed to try to support them both, as well as provide the equipment and live sound for one of them as they were completely new to this. Not only that, but I'd also need to figure out the travel arrangements. It was proving to be a costly venture.

I'd had an idea of creating merchandise to sell for the artist to earn money. I thought I'd let the artists keep whatever they'd earned and I'd help assist in the design and manufacturing of the product in China. Peter still wasn't at all keen on me travelling while pregnant, with no clue of how the equipment would be set up and put away. Oh, the pressures of management. On the licensing side, I was getting more and more placements with great TV shows in the US and Mexico so everything was coming together and flowing really well in every area of my life. I really was truly happy. The only thing was, I couldn't shake this nagging, persistent pain in my side.

I was starting to feel the symptoms of pregnancy now that I was a few weeks in. I was needing to sleep during the day. Well, it seemed like all hours of the day sometimes and the morning sickness had really started to kick in. I was grateful for it though as in my mind it confirmed the pregnancy was developing as healthily as it should. I was also starting to show slightly. I seemed to need to eat every hour to keep nausea at bay, although I was never actually physically sick. The only thing I found that could take the pain away was trying to sleep.

Surely pregnancy wasn't supposed to feel painful? I learned about round ligaments stretching and causing discomfort, but this was almost agonising at times. I wondered if it was because I had had three surgeries the previous year and there was scar tissue healing. I went to the doctors, and they referred me to the Early Pregnancy Unit, so I had an eight-week scan to see if they could find anything. They couldn't. They told me everything seemed normal and the heartbeat was there. A nurse took me into a room and said perhaps the concern from the previous ectopic was causing me to panic and not to worry as everything looked normal. I tried to take her comforting words on board, but something was still nagging at me that things weren't right.

Meanwhile, it was summer and we had Peter's birthday to celebrate. His family came down to visit and we all went to a local festival of chillies. It was a fun day out and we watched a chilli-eating competition which looked brutal. We headed on back to the house later in the evening and Peter and his family proceeded to celebrate and enjoy a few drinks, but I was shattered as normal so stuck earplugs in and went off to sleep at 9 p.m. That was late for me during pregnancy. It definitely felt satisfying in the morning when everyone came down with headaches.

I took it easy as I had a singing showcase that I hosted every two months for all the singers I managed and vocalists I coached. I was due to play keys for around ten singers so needed last-minute prep and assistance in setting everything up at the venue. I was concerned I'd forget what I was playing as everything seemed to feel like such a foggy haze all the time. I didn't even think baby brain existed at ten weeks, which is what I was at this point.

It was a special showcase too as one of the guitarists, *Antony, who happened to be a great friend of mine, and his wife were performing. We were like family and did lots together with them and their children and they made a fantastic duo in every sense. This time Antony was also going to sing his first solo performance.

I did make one or two mistakes in the end, but I don't think anyone noticed. Antony sang a cover of 'Candle In The Wind' and performed amazingly. I felt super proud as it'd taken him all these years to sing on his own in front of others. He had all eyes and ears on him in the room, which was packed out. Little did I know, it would be not only the last time I'd see him perform but the last time I'd see him alive.

It was time for my twelve-week scan, and I couldn't believe how fast it had come around. It was to be at the maternity hospital, so I was super proud that I'd graduated from the Early Pregnancy Unit to the actual maternity hospital now. It felt like I had the stamp of approval of a fully-fledged pregnancy. Peter, unfortunately, couldn't take the time off work as he'd recently started a new job, and I figured it was just a routine scan. I'd had my last one a few weeks before so it'd be fine to just go on my own.

I was a bit saddened once I'd reached the hospital and looked around and saw mainly couples sitting together eagerly awaiting their scan. Oh well, I thought there'll be plenty of others. I was called in by a female nurse and taken into a scanning room with a bed in the middle and all the scanning equipment next to it along with a big TV monitor screen facing the bed.

As I was now twelve weeks along, she only needed to do a tummy scan which made me glad as I hated having to strip off my bottoms and wear a paper towel all the time! It was a lot less invasive than an internal scan. As she prepared my tummy with the gel, she made chitchat by asking me about myself, my pregnancy, how it'd been going and proceeded to do the scan. I could immediately see my baby on the large screen in front of me and I was smiling as he/she had grown a lot since the last scan and looked like a baby now, although, still small.

The nurse was quiet but then proceeded to ask me how many weeks I thought I was and when my last scan was. I told her I had a scan at eight weeks and that I was now twelve weeks along. She continued to look at the screen in silence before putting the scanning equipment down, turning to me and saying, 'I'm really sorry, but it's not good news today, I'm afraid. I've checked a few times, but there doesn't seem to be a heartbeat.' It's still difficult writing this now. Anyone that has experienced this or similar knows how traumatic it is.

I listened while she continued to explain that she'd thoroughly checked for a heartbeat, but the result was the same. I replied, 'What do you mean?' I felt completely dumbfounded, in complete shock. She said the baby measured ten weeks, not twelve, and it seemed that the baby had stopped growing and the heart had stopped beating at ten weeks.

I thought it was a joke, or a mistake. My baby had been fine a few weeks ago. How could this be? My mind couldn't even process or comprehend what was being said to me. The nurse explained that she would get a second opinion and disappeared off to find someone and at that moment my phone began ringing. It was my sister. I just burst into tears and told her I suddenly felt so alone. I had no one with me and was faced with a miscarriage. She felt really upset too and tried to comfort me.

The nurse came back with another female nurse so I told my sister I had to go and hung up. The second nurse introduced herself and explained she would do an internal examination so I would need to empty my bladder. My eyes felt red and face puffy from crying. I hadn't realised that I would have to walk past all the mums-to-be and their partners in the waiting room to get to the toilet, which was degrading. I'd never felt so alone in my life.

The nurse did the internal scan but came to the same conclusion: the baby's heartbeat had stopped at ten weeks. They took me into a private room and asked if I had anyone with me. I explained I didn't, and they looked sorry for me. I sat in the room alone and felt like my whole world had come crashing down around me. How was I here again? How did it get to this? What did I do wrong? Was it something I ate, something I did? I had no warning signs at all that this was going to happen. I rang Peter and explained what had happened and how I felt so alone having to hear this and go through this on my own, and why didn't he just take the day off? Why was that more important than what I had to endure? I think I was looking for something or someone to blame. The truth was it was no one's fault. He asked if I needed him to come to the hospital, but I explained I'd be heading home shortly so there was no point.

The nurse came in and explained in a soft tone that I'd experienced a silent miscarriage, which meant that my body hadn't registered the baby had died, so was still producing pregnancy hormones and symptoms. How could life be so cruel? I left the hospital and sat in my car and just cried and cried. I didn't know what to do, where to go or who I needed to be with me or if I needed to be alone. I felt like I didn't even want to be in my body at this moment. I was all over the place.

Looking back, I was in a complete state of shock. Never had I factored in miscarriage ever being something I'd also be suffering. I had truly thought that now that my tubes were out, IVF was the answer, and everything had been going so well...it just didn't make sense, not one single bit.

I called my best friend *Jess and told her to meet me at the house. I got back and Peter was there to give me a big hug and told me none of this was our fault and that he was sorry he wasn't there but neither of us expected it to end up like this. He asked if I wanted him to spend the rest of the day with me, but I explained I was meeting Jess as I really just needed my best friend with me at this moment.

We went to the pub and—many may find this completely wrong—but I got completely drunk. I just wanted to numb all feelings and escape reality. I knew my baby wasn't alive so nothing could harm it otherwise I would never have touched anything potentially harmful to the baby. I just needed to block everything out for a while. I couldn't move past the fact I was carrying my dead baby inside me. I even still looked pregnant.

Blocking out my feelings helped momentarily. Jess and I had long chats and I said to her how I just didn't see it coming at all. How had I lost three babies in the space of a year? She took me to visit my horse. Anyone who has a pet, especially horses, knows the deep bond and connection you have. Pets are literally the best therapy!

We sat in the field and my horse wouldn't leave my side the whole time, for hours. Normally I'd just get ignored unless I had carrots. It's strange how animals have such a deep sense of your emotions and comfort you when you're sad. I'll never forget that moment. He's a truly special horse and I'm so lucky to have the connection with him that I do. He's seen me through so many traumas, changes and tragedies. It was around 7 p.m. when Jess dropped me home and I just went to bed and slept and slept, not wanting to ever wake and face the world.

TWENTY
New Stars In The Sky

*'I carried you for every second of your life,
and I will love you every second of mine'*

Peter and I were back at the Early Pregnancy Unit to discuss options for terminating the pregnancy. None of the options seemed desirable, but I knew I needed to choose one, so I opted for the surgical route which would involve being put under anaesthetic and the doctor clearing out the 'contents' such as the embryo and pregnancy tissue, etc. I just couldn't believe that it was only a few days earlier that everything had been fine and now I was going back into my fourth surgery in a year for a miscarriage.

Our family and friends were just as heartbroken as we were, and couldn't understand it either as everything had been going so well. I tried to research about miscarriages and read that they were very common and that it was normally down to abnormal chromosomes within the embryo. I came round from the surgery and still felt numb. I remember sleeping a lot and trying to recover as much as possible. My only salvation was knowing we could try again and still had another round on the NHS.

The hospital strongly advised I receive counselling which they'd provide due to the fact I'd had a few losses. I was offered it previously but was always of the opinion that working through it myself was the better option. Perhaps they were right. Maybe I would try it and see if it would help. I did end up taking the counselling, but I didn't find it made a massive difference. I know it works well for some people, but I found I got just as much from talking to my friends. I was lucky I had a good support group.

It was difficult to discuss it with Peter. I think the reason was because we were both hurting and his idea of getting through things was to bury himself in work. I also found that to be the answer for me most of the time, although looking back now, keeping myself busy only delayed feelings of grief and the feelings surfaced at times of quietness or at later times if they hadn't been dealt with.

I decided I was going to go on the artist tour that was starting in a few weeks and thought perhaps being away and having a change of scenery would do me good. There was a lot of driving involved and it would be heavy going but keeping my mind occupied would be good for me. What I didn't know was that, before the tour started, the month of August would actually turn out to be one of the worst in my whole life and one I will not forget in a hurry.

Shortly after my miscarriage, I received a call from one of my best friends who had emigrated to New Zealand ten years previously to tell me my ex-boyfriend (the one I told you about at the start of the book, and whom I'd spent the best part of ten years with) had passed away from brain cancer. We knew it was going to happen at some point as he'd been battling it for a few years, but it still blindsided me when I heard it.

I was floored. I not only had my baby to mourn but now my childhood boyfriend as well. The funeral was hard. I went on my own as Peter didn't particularly want to go which I could understand. Even though it was from way back in my past, I knew I'd regret it if I didn't go. Lots of my old friends from my childhood were there, but it was very emotional, and later looking through all the old photos of me and others during the wake was very difficult. I bawled my eyes out driving back home and thought about all the old times we used to have, good and bad. I couldn't believe he'd been taken so young. We went through so much together and I knew I'd never get the chance to ever see him again.

I just didn't know how to handle all the losses, and would find myself randomly bursting into tears. In the midst of that, I needed to go to the IVF clinic for a follow-up appointment which turned out to be a waste of time as it seemed they'd forgotten they were expecting me. The consultant didn't seem to have read my notes beforehand, and all he could offer was, 'We don't know the reasons behind why things like this happen.' Yeah, thanks. I just drove forty-five minutes for you to tell me *things like this happen*. My only saving grace, at this time, was getting out into nature on my horse and trying to think of positive times ahead, keeping hold of hope.

Unfortunately, things were about to get even worse. About a fortnight later, Peter and I went to a boozy BBQ and had a great time. But the next day I felt horribly sick from consuming too much. I slept most of the day on the sofa, but when I awoke, around 9 p.m., I found lots of missed calls from *Gail (my friend from the showcase I told you about earlier). I listened to her voicemail and through the desperation in her voice, she sobbed, 'Antony's died.' I can't remember what else was on the voicemail as I was in complete shock. How can this be real, he was literally singing at my showcase a few days earlier? I tried to call back but couldn't reach her. Peter and I spent the evening completely horror-struck.

I rushed round to her house the next day, where she and the kids were being comforted by family and it was such a heart-rending, distressing day. Everyone was inconsolable and I was trying my hardest to stay sto-ic—I have always struggled to show emotions in front of others. As it turned out, his death was the result of a tragic accident at home. I'm not going to go into details, but it was another day that will stay with me forever. Life wouldn't be the same with our dear friend taken from us and forced to leave behind his family.

I tried to help in any way I could by making meals and taking them round even though I knew no one could eat. I just wanted to do something. It was such a traumatic time and I didn't even know where to begin processing all that had happened within the space of one short month. I pushed the loss of my baby aside while I tried to be there for my best friend and her family, but I was also trying to mourn the loss of my ex-partner. I don't think I ever did get the chance to truly mourn the loss of my baby. I was filled with so much grief and sadness that I went into a deep state of depression without realising. It took a while for me to come out of it.

TWENTY-ONE
A Much-Needed Break

*'You may have to fight a battle
more than once to win it'*

Peter and I decided to book ourselves a holiday after such a horrendous month and to try to pick ourselves up while taking some time out. We both needed to get our strength back and chose Greece as a holiday destination. We went to Agassi, staying in a really nice boutique, luxurious hotel. We arrived in the early hours of the morning, which still felt like the middle of the night as it was pitch black. We had to sleep on the sun loungers by the pool until our room was ready later on that day.

It was beautiful to wake up to the sunrise, though, and just having a change of scenery instantly helped my emotions. Our apartment had a balcony overlooking the pool and views of the beautiful, crystal-clear blue sea. The hotel was situated on a really steep hill so walking anywhere was a bit of a challenge, but we ventured into the small town and ate, did some sunbathing then decided to get a few bottles of wine and sit on the balcony playing cards and listening to music. It was so great to reconnect, switch off and just remember what it was like to have fun again without having to think of what meds to take, having to watch your diet, having pregnancy symptoms making you sleep all the time and just to remember life before all of this started. We truly did have such a great day.

We got pretty tipsy but I think letting our hair down was exactly what was needed. We talked about so much and checked in with one another about how we were truly feeling which we hadn't done in a while. It felt nice to be back reconnected once again. The weather was beautiful, sunny and hot. We then moved on to Zante and rented an apartment right on the beach. We avoided the strip like the plague, aware it was a place where teens went with their mates on holiday. But the beach area and all the bars were lovely, so we spent most evenings eating at different restaurants trying out the cuisines. Our days were filled with tours and exploring the island, which was spectacular, and we also took a boat trip.

The Greek islands are truly beautiful and we felt as though we were in paradise; the food was so good and the people were nice too. We saw turtles and swam in caves. We saw the iconic shipwreck and went horse riding—in the sea, although the horses didn't want to do much swimming and refused to move. We came back from the holiday completely re-energised, and I felt ready to start my artist's tour.

It was strange staying in so many different hotels and there was so much driving involved. It really was exhausting, loading and unloading equipment—sometimes twice a day if we had two venues in one day where the artist was performing. It was also a nightmare if there was a tech issue and there was a lot of pressure to sort it out by the time the audience arrived. We were really cutting it fine at one of the venues. It was a nice distraction and was a lot of fun driving across Wales, but sometimes the pressure of organising it, managing the artist and being responsible for all the sound and equipment was a lot, especially when I was still mourning so many losses from the previous month.

With all the stress of seeing through the tours of two artists separately, by the last venue we were all truly exhausted. I was beyond burnt-out in every sense. Once I arrived back home after two months it was time to throw ourselves back into IVF treatment. Peter was happy for me to make the decision and take lead on it. I felt in my mind that throwing myself back into it all would help me recover from the loss and replace the baby I had lost.

In reality, and in hindsight, it just doesn't work out like that, not for me anyway. I was in denial, insisting that I was truly ready and healed. In my mind I figured that when something doesn't work, you have to try and try again and keep trying until it does work, but when it came to IVF and Mother Nature, I didn't have that kind of control, no matter how hard I tried.

Sometimes, it felt like I was continuously banging my head against a wall while expecting a different result.

TWENTY - TWO
IVF Round Two!

*'Your story is the key that can
unlock someone's prison'*

I don't remember a huge amount about the second IVF cycle as I was very emotionally distant and cut off from the whole process. I went into it feeling completely detached, not caring if it worked or not. I think I was trying to protect myself and ultimately shut myself down. I hadn't truly healed, and my mind, body and spirit weren't in the best place for a gruelling IVF schedule and all the emotional turmoil that comes with it.

Looking back, I knew deep down it wasn't the right time, but I chose to ignore my inner feelings. I didn't feel positive or negative about the whole process, I just felt numb, as though I was going through the motions. I did everything that was asked of me, and Peter helped to give me the injections again. My body responded well to the treatment plan and the consultants said we had a great grade five blastocyst they would implant. First it would be thawed out then transferred into my womb.

A FET cycle (frozen embryo transfer) is slightly easier than the fresh IVF cycle as most of the hard work has already been done the first time around, so it's a case of preparing your body for your embryo transfer. This was a medicated cycle so again. I took Buserelin to essentially switch off the hormones, then oestrogen tablets which prepares the womb lining and gets the lining nice and thick, ready for transfer.

In both IVF cycles, I'd then be given progesterone pessaries, which can cause irritation, and I had to wear pads constantly as they're messy and leak! I had to forget about sex for a while as I couldn't mix the two. These pessaries need to be taken for up to three months to help support any pregnancy, but obviously, if I'd received a negative result then I would have stopped taking them. We received a call the morning of transfer day to say that our embryo had thawed successfully which was great news.

We went in and the same process followed. We could watch the transfer of our embryo on a screen in front of us as the doctor successfully implanted the embryo into the womb lining. We were excited, but also cautious without the false sense of security this time. I was half expecting it not to work. The days following the two-week wait, I kept myself very busy and tried not to think about it. I wasn't even tempted to test early. I just thought I'd await the day of the blood test and let the clinic tell me if it had been successful. It hadn't.

We received the call after I went to the clinic for the blood test to say that unfortunately, the treatment had been unsuccessful. Peter was home and I immediately informed him of the outcome. He said 'Well, it's better to know early on'. He was right, though I did feel a bit saddened and had a little cry. But I had also been detached from the whole thing throughout the entire process. Bad news had just become something I expected when it came to this, for both of us.

The actual devastating blow was that we had now used up our funding on the NHS, so would need to pay for any further treatment ourselves. We had two embryos left in storage but by this point, we'd both been through enough and just needed a break from it all. I knew I was physically and mentally exhausted. I don't even think my body was in a position to carry a pregnancy at this point.

TWENTY-THREE
A Time for Healing

*'The Soul Always Knows What
to Do to Heal Itself'*

Peter and I had six months off treatment, babies, and anything at all related to them. I was so thankful for it. I'd finally succumbed to putting my body and mind at rest and allowing myself to just switch off and recharge. It was during this time I realised that I had completely forgotten what it was like just to live, and to have fun and reconnect with those around me.

I was a person with goals and dreams before all this IVF baby stuff. A person who was career-focused; loved my work; enjoyed time with friends; travelling; eating good food; cooking; wine; horse riding; long walks; spending time with family; creating new ideas and seeing them come to life; time with my partner; visiting new places or just enjoying being lazy together at home. I'd forgotten that I'd had a life before I became all too consumed with needing/wanting a baby to complete me. I only realised this when I took that break for six months and it was to be a further twelve months before I threw myself back into IVF treatment again. I became grateful for all the people in my life and things that made my life fulfilling.

Yes, I really wanted to be a mother, but I could also enjoy a fulfilling life in the meantime. And if it came to it. and if kids weren't meant for me, then I had enough in my life to still be happy. I counted my blessings: I had my health, my family with both sets of parents even if they hadn't been together since I was young, sister, great friends, a partner, and I was still to enjoy a wedding day in the future, although I wasn't in any rush. I had my animals, a great career and was one decision away from any life I wanted (within reason). I'd weathered through many struggles and hardships before and was pretty resilient, so I wasn't going to let fertility struggles ruin my life.

It really saddened me to think of all the years I'd spent wishing my life away on a baby. Yes, I really wanted it to happen but was my life really worthless without one? I did a lot of soul-searching and through the process became so much happier and more positive about the whole thing. I reconnected properly with Peter because, even for a short while, having all the pressure and expectation removed from our relationship had made a huge difference, and we enjoyed each other's company again. I remembered how much I enjoyed my work and started making fantastic progress with my film/tv placements and had more music in TV shows and films across the world.

I got to a place of true happiness again by letting go for a while and just enjoying life, and it truly felt good. Most importantly, I allowed myself the time to heal...finally. Heal from all the losses and traumas that I hadn't allowed myself to recover from previously as I was constantly jumping from one IVF cycle to the next; one loss to the next; one surgery to the next. I felt apologetic for what I had pushed my body through, too, in such a short space of time. I didn't want to get to a time when perhaps I had reached my dream of having my babies then realised I'd wasted years in despair not enjoying life because I'd become so fixated on this one thing, and had ignored my freedom to enjoy all the rest.

If you allow it, you can lose yourself completely and quickly spiral into a state of depression, becoming an unrecognisable shadow of your former self, so I knew it was really important to take a big step back. I ate what I liked and drank what I liked without any guilt or remorse, and it felt great. I also cut out the things in my life that were no longer working.

I simplified things by deciding I would only manage one artist, and only until the remaining singles were re-leased. It had become too much pressure and too much hassle to develop and manage an artist from scratch and I just wasn't getting the same satisfaction from it any more. The negatives seemed to be outweighing the positives and there just wasn't enough financial return in respect to the amount of work that needed to go in.

I felt saddened by this as I'd spent many years developing and launching new artists and it felt great seeing them grow and prosper after taking them under my wing, like polishing a diamond in the rough, but it was time to move on to new projects. I also found I was in a place of strength and happiness again and I was able to assist others. When a lady reached out to me, who had recently suffered her second ectopic shortly before her wedding day, and was feeling absolutely distraught and lost, I was able to connect with her.

She had one remaining tube but was terrified of getting pregnant again. I completely understood and shared her fear as I had felt that way after my first ectopic. I offered her words of comfort and told her my story, but also told her that although I still wasn't pregnant I was full of hope that it would happen one day and that the fact she got pregnant was a great sign that she could in the future. Time is a great healer and I suggested she talk about her feelings and not give up hope for her future as sometimes that's all we have in times of turmoil when there's nothing real to grasp on to. It's hope that pushes us to keep trying against all the odds, not knowing what the outcome will be. She found strength in my words, and we've kept in touch since.

She eventually did become pregnant with her remaining tube with her baby growing in the right place this time. I always said to those close to me, going through the losses and trauma is all worth it if I can pass on comfort, hope and strength to others through my story. It helped me to find strength in others who had suffered similarly and to find comfort in their words.

Your story is powerful. Share it if you can.

TWENTY-FOUR
A Greek Love Affair!

*'We must free ourselves of the hope
that the sea will ever rest. We must
learn to sail in high winds'*

After six months of enjoying life and getting to a place of strength, I felt mentally and physically ready to start looking into our third round of IVF. It felt completely different going into it this time as I truly felt strong enough to go through the process again. I was emotionally ready (as ready as I could be).

I started to spend a lot of time researching different clinics not just in the UK, but in Europe too as I knew treatment could be cheaper than the UK, and even more advanced in some cases. There were two embryos left, and we needed to give it a go with what we had left. I also thought that I would have two embryos transferred this time and Peter didn't dispute that. I figured it'd save costs on further treatment and could perhaps increase my chances. I knew there were many warnings in the UK about transferring more than one, but I was willing to take the risk. I also wondered if I could even grow two babies as I was only five feet one inch tall. Was it physically even possible?

I also wanted to get to the bottom of why the miscarriage happened and why the cycle failed because there didn't seem to be an obvious reason. I knew my ectopic pregnancies were because of my blocked tubes, but the consultants and I reckoned that the problem had been removed so the path should have been clear. After spending a few months looking and reading reviews on forums, checking stats on the top ten IVF clinics in Europe and reading up as much as I could, I eventually settled on an IVF clinic in Athens. I was truly excited when I found this clinic as it had five-star reviews everywhere and was in the top five official list of most recommended clinics in Europe.

The clinic also seemed to have had success when dealing with the most difficult cases. I knew in my heart this was the place I wanted to go. I had the money saved up purely for treatment costs, and once again, I felt that glimmer of hope and the feeling that this could be it. I discussed the details about the clinic with Peter, and offered to put the money into it as I really wanted to try and I didn't want there to be any reason why we weren't able to go ahead. Neither of us wanted to stay at the clinic we were at for any more cycles. We had had to use the previous clinic as it was funded on the NHS, but now we had an array of options. Except...

It turned out that he wasn't in a rush to try again and wasn't at all enamoured by the idea. I think he'd had enough of it all. I put my case across and explained I would organise everything and fund it all, that it seemed a waste to just leave the embryos in storage. Plus, it's better to do it when you can rather than wait, considering my age, as I was now heading towards thirty-six. He still wasn't enamoured by it, but didn't say no flat out, so I decided to at least have a consultation with the clinic to see what they had to say.

A lovely Greek lady called *Athanasia was the main doctor at the clinic who spoke with me and we went through my previous fertility history and she explained she had achieved a lot of results with others in my situation. She suggested I have some testing done first to see if there was an issue that hadn't been picked up yet, and I explained that I was thinking of moving my embryos from the UK to their clinic in Athens. She advised against it, saying it would be costly.

A better idea might be to have the testing done in Athens and be treated there and to then be ready for transfer back at the clinic in the UK. I didn't want to choose that option though; my mind was made up. I wanted to either go into this whole-heartedly or not at all. I also liked that they were the only IVF clinic not to suggest putting me straight in for IVF treatment without checking for issues first. They seemed genuinely concerned about getting to the bottom of why my miscarriage and failed cycle happened previously by suggesting that I undergo more fertility testing, something that wasn't offered in the UK. They actually cared about getting results.

I felt the huge spark of excitement that this was the answer to my fertility issues. If any clinic could help me then it was this one. The clinic suggested that I should have my menstrual blood tested first for any hidden infections. This freaked me out a bit at first and sounded pretty gross. But it was also a necessary evil. I needed to send off my menstrual blood to the clinic in Greece to be tested and I would then receive the results by email.

I had to make sure it was wrapped super tight as no postman wanted to deal with that kind of leakage on the job. It's also not an easy task getting a sample in the first place. The lengths we go to in this fertility club! Nothing, in particular, came up in the results aside from a very low level of good bacteria, only 12% so I needed a serious boost. They suggested probiotics and I was then advised on having a hysteroscopy with implantation cuts and Chicago immunology tests done.

A hysteroscopy is a simple procedure where I was placed under general anaesthetic while a gynaecological surgeon looked inside of my womb to diagnose and treat any issues. At the same time the surgeon performed small cuts at the top of my uterus to help rejuvenate the womb lining and increase implantation rates. The Chicago immunology tests were to check for natural killer cells and other things to see if my immune system was perceiving an embryo as a threat then attacking it and causing a miscarriage. All in all, the investigations were to cost me over £2500, not including the cost of the trip, but I figured the cost was an investment into my fertility health and would be worth it to get to the bottom of why my loss and last IVF cycle failed.

There was definitely tension at home as I felt Peter didn't want to go ahead with it but understood that I had to have these tests done regardless as it was my reproductive health at stake, and I needed to do it. He had said he'd come with me, but we didn't really discuss anything to do with IVF as it had become a touchy subject.

Meanwhile, I continued with plans to start the process of moving the embryos from the UK to Greece as a lot of paperwork was involved. The clinic in Athens had a specialist courier they preferred to use and the package needed to be transported by an embryologist who was an expert in handling embryos and transporting them—hence the cost of £1000. That was the most expensive plane flight I'd ever taken and I wasn't even going to be on it.

The embryos were to be hand-delivered and kept in liquid nitrogen tanks at −196°C and would avoid X-ray machines to avoid damage. The process, they told me, would take a few months to complete before they could go anywhere as there was to be a lot of organising and paperwork for the clinics on both sides.

In the meantime, Peter and I were preparing for our first trip to Athens which we were quite excited about. I'd found an apartment to stay for five days whilst I had my surgery. Something didn't seem right between us though; Peter seemed really stressed and had been throwing himself into work and seemed distant from me.

Two days before we were due to leave, we were heading out to get some last-minute bits and to change money, etc., when he seemed to get more and more irritated with me over nothing in particular. It's always the small things you bicker about in relationships when in fact they are a mask for the real issues you're really arguing about.

The bickering got more and more heated on this particular day; then we realised we'd left something at home we needed before we could actually get to the supermarket, which didn't help matters. I decided there and then it was pointless going out with emotions high like this.

I got out of the car and told Peter I wasn't going to the supermarket and just went inside the house. He stormed upstairs and stayed there for the rest of the day until the evening when he decided to come down and went into the kitchen. I figured we needed to sort this as we'd be leaving on a plane in two days and we weren't even speaking to each other.

I couldn't even remember what had started the argument, but I knew deep down it was the pressures of another IVF cycle and the thought of me going ahead with it when his heart wasn't in it. He had his back to me and I said to him assertively, 'Look, we need to sort whatever's going on here as we're leaving in two days and it's not going to be a holiday. I'm going for surgery and need to know that I can rest during recovery and be certain there won't be any arguments.'

He had his back facing me, palms down on the kitchen worktop with his head lowered and there was a long, uncomfortable silence while I was trying to figure out what his response would be. At the same time, I was adamant that I was going to stand my ground on this.

He still kept his back toward me as he said through gritted teeth, 'You just fucking irritate me. I'm not sure I want to be in this any more'. I was floored. I was not expecting that response at all. I needed to get out of the house as quickly as I could, but I responded in a calm but icy tone, 'We're leaving in two days, I'm undergoing surgery and you're telling me this now! You've had plenty of time to tell me you didn't want to go or that you don't want to be with me!'

I immediately left the house and went up to see my horse and just let the emotion out. I was so angry. I know there are always two sides to an argument and two different viewpoints and I'm not trying to blame anybody here. I'm simply relaying what was said and at the same time to recognise that, in hindsight, I was pushing him into another round of treatment when all along he'd said he didn't want to do it. He wanted to wait and I didn't listen and went ahead anyway. Emotions were bound to get to boiling point and reach a pressure point with all the stress of another looming cycle impending.

I was frantic, trying to decide what to do. I figured I couldn't go to Greece with all that uncertainty weighing over me, and so I decided to find a backup and to get someone else to come on the trip with me just in case, and perhaps we'd sort things out anyway. Later that evening, after we'd both calmed down, he said he didn't mean what he'd said, and he still wanted to go. I said we needed to write down all the things that we needed to communicate with each other and to go through it the next evening as there were clearly things that needed to be said, but right now was not the time.

The next day, I was out all day and when I came home Peter was also out but had exchanged the money which was positive. I messaged him to see where he was as we were supposed to have a discussion and he responded that he was at a friend's and wanted to chill there longer. I explained that we had things we needed to sort out and had agreed to have a chat as nothing had been sorted between us and we were due to leave the next day. He said we would chat once he was home but wanted to stay out longer.

I hit the roof and told him to just stay out and decided there and then if he wasn't home in the next hour, I'd be going to Greece without him. He was home in the evening but by that time I'd made my decision and had been on the phone to my mum and bought her a ticket to Athens.

I don't think he ever expected me to act on my anger, but it was important to me to have a serious chat to discuss issues and that hadn't gone ahead. Plus, at the time, it felt like he wasn't taking it seriously. I told him the new plans and decided that he wouldn't be going to Greece because I needed to know I could have a restful time as I'd be recovering from surgery and did not want to run the risk of another fall-out. I suggested we have a long think and would reconvene once I was back. I was still so angry.

I flew out the next day and met my mum at Athens airport as she lived in Cyprus. We took a taxi to the apartment, which turned out to be quite nice but a bit of a walk to the clinic. Athens looked like a great place, busy and had some really nice and not so nice areas, like anywhere really. They had beautiful olive and orange trees! It was difficult to enjoy though as I still felt sad that Peter and I weren't on the trip together.

The next day I had a consultation at the clinic and the consultant advised me I'd need to have tests done at the local hospital to check I was fit enough for surgery the next day and that I needed to also be at the local hospital for 6 a.m. 6 a.m? Seriously! I was still tired from travelling. I was to then travel back to the clinic after my surgery to go through the findings for a review and to discuss next steps. I also had blood tests done shortly after my consultation for my Chicago tests. These came back normal which was a relief.

Mum and I headed off in a taxi to the local hospital, which was a fifteen-minute drive, for my preliminary tests. It was a huge, white building and very clean inside which was good to note. I went to reception and was met with an icy greeting from the receptionist. She spoke very quickly and I struggled to understand what she was saying in her thick, Greek accent.

She quickly became frustrated with me and spoke in a deliberate, slowed down tone with a sarcastic undertone to it—so much so that the second receptionist stood next to her shot her a look and glanced back at me with an apologetic look on her face. I was glad that it wasn't just me that acknowledged the bitchy greeting. It was unnecessary. I thought about complaining but figured it wasn't worth it. I just hoped my surgeon would be a lot nicer. I get that I was English and hardly knew any Greek, but I was paying a lot of money to use their services, and surely it's customer service 101 to be nice to paying customers.

Mum and I waited to be seen by the doctor which took quite a while. Eventually, we were the last ones to be called. I went in on my own and was told to lie down on the bed in a room I was taken into by a female doctor, who also came off quite blunt and rude with her directions. I soon figured perhaps it was just different here than back home and their bedside manner was unlike our hospitals in the UK. I definitely didn't feel welcome, that was for sure.

She abruptly told me to remove my top half of clothing and she monitored my heart. I wasn't given any further instruction, then all of a sudden, she drew the curtain slightly and proceeded to leave the room abruptly without telling me she was off while I was left with half my clothes missing. I panicked and shouted after her, 'Do I need to put my clothes back on?' She responded curtly, 'No' then walked out of the door, pushing it wide open so I was in full view of everyone in the waiting room. I was desperately trying to cover my modesty! I was horrified!

Before I had a chance to react, another person walked into my room and luckily it turned out to be another doctor. I was glad that it wasn't a random person as I felt very vulnerable. He ran a couple more tests then told me to get dressed and said all was fine for the surgery the following day. I breathed a sigh of relief that I could get out of this place and felt panicked that my surgery might be met with the same level of frostiness and lack of bedside manner. Looking back now, I probably should've complained, but I wanted to get in and get out as quickly as possible. Perhaps things were just different to how we did things back home.

I wasn't to have any breakfast or anything to eat or drink after midnight. My mum and I decided to ask the waitress, at the restaurant where we ate that evening, to book a taxi for us to arrive for 5:30 a.m. as we were concerned it might not arrive if *we* booked it.

After a restless sleep not knowing what to expect, we dragged ourselves out of bed, got ready and waited at the bottom of the road for the taxi hoping that it would turn up. Luckily it did. It was still pitch black when we arrived at the hospital and it was eerily quiet. We went to the surgery admissions department, filled out the forms and paid for the surgery. I was then taken into a cubicle for last-minute checks and was told to wait until it was time and a nurse would come to collect me. I

I kept reminding myself that they do surgeries all the time and the clinic got great results. I needed to put my bad experiences behind and get on with it. A nurse came and explained that they were going to take me to wait outside the operating room to be prepped for surgery. I was wheeled on my hospital bed, and I felt very nervous by this point, especially as everyone was talking in Greek and I didn't understand anything. I really needed to learn more of the language coming back next time!

Suddenly we came to an abrupt stop and the nurse wandered off without saying anything. I was left on my bed in a hallway. I thought I'd be taken into a room, but I was left in a corridor with lots of doctors and nurses walking past me. I felt so out of place and longed to be anywhere but there. I felt so alone by this point. I really had a newfound appreciation for our NHS hospitals and our bedside manner.

A new nurse I hadn't seen before came along and started to put a cannula in my hand without first giving any explanation of what she was about to do. Luckily, I'd had enough surgeries to know what process was needed beforehand. She continued to talk to her friend nearby, barely acknowledging me, then walked off once she was done.

Next, a man who looked in his late forties, with dark mid-length hair and tanned skin, very Greek-looking, came over and introduced himself as *Dr Papadopoulos and explained he would be doing my surgery today. He talked me through the procedure and asked me if I had any questions. Finally, I thought. Someone who gives me explanations and makes me feel comforted. I felt a lot more secure going into the surgery after meeting him and he had a very calm demeanour about him.

I was then wheeled into the operating room and asked to get onto the gurney and to put my feet in stirrups. Gulp! There were around five people in the room who were nurses assisting with the operation. I had an anaesthetist putting me under general anaesthetic, then I remember waking up in the operating room and asking to be put under again. Funny what those drugs do to you. I must've been having a good time whilst being out of it, whatever I was doing! I was taken into another room to come round and then my mum helped me back to the clinic, while I clutched a DVD of my surgery that I could watch later.

I still felt so woozy and out of it, but at the IVF clinic the doctor and I watched through the DVD and it was very strange to see the inside of my womb and watch the incisions being made. She said all looked fine, no cause for concern so there was no specific reason she could find to explain why my last miscarriage and failed IVF cycle happened. The only other reason could be down to the embryos. I had read that the majority of miscarriages were down to abnormal chromosomes. Either way, she said she wasn't concerned about any future cycles potentially not working as all looked okay. I felt positive about this news and went back home and slept for the rest of the day.

The next day, Mum and I went to visit the Acropolis and went exploring, although my tummy hurt a bit from surgery the previous day, so I was probably being a little too adventurous when I should've been resting. I received an email through from the courier company to say all looked good for the transport of the embryos within the next few days and I confirmed with the clinic in Athens that I'd be due to start my next cycle the following month. I couldn't believe how quickly it was coming together. Implantation cuts were also more successful when an embryo was implanted within the next month or two.

It was finally our last night in Athens and we went to our favourite new restaurant at the end of our road, when suddenly something seemed completely different. There was a huge panic in the air and all the staff around us in the restaurant seemed to be very stressed. We were the only people in there too which seemed strange.

Outside seemed deserted and it felt like we'd just walked into a zombie apocalypse or something. We asked the waiter if something was going on as he was rushing around like a headless chicken, and he exclaimed that they'd been given notice at the restaurant that day to shut down completely. The whole of Athens was locking down and all businesses were closing temporarily because of Covid with no indication of how long they would have to stay that way.

Wow, I knew Covid was causing a lot of problems, but back home travel wasn't restricted, and we were only told to wash our hands and keep our distance. No talk of a lockdown had ever been mentioned. Perhaps we were next? I felt lucky that we were leaving the next morning otherwise we might have been stuck there. If this was getting a lot more serious, then my embryos needed to move quickly.

TWENTY-FIVE
Enter Lockdown!

*'The past is passed, the present is paused
and the future will be well played'*

Peter came to pick me up from the airport, with his family, when I landed in London. Although there was a bit of tension after the arguments we had before I'd left, and the fact he hadn't come with me, we wanted to move past it as there were enough stressful things going on at the time.

Not long after I arrived back from Greece, lockdown came into full effect in the UK too. This was pretty devastating as my embryos weren't able to travel anywhere and treatment was to be put on hold for the indefinite future until the virus eased up. It was difficult to process after finally getting somewhere and making progress. Plus, the implantation cuts were most effective within two months of the transfer.

But there wasn't anything that could be done. It was completely out of my control. Many people were suffering a lot worse than just not being able to undergo treatment, and so I focused on gratitude for not having lost anyone around me from Covid and still having clients to bring in an income when others were losing their jobs and businesses. I decided to throw myself into a new business project for an idea I had.

The number of my clients had halved overnight, and I realised I needed to put my energies into building something new. The film industry came to an abrupt halt in filming, and the live side for artists performing was suddenly non-existent.

These were new, crazy times we found ourselves in, but the comforting thing was that we were now all in this together. Everyone was suffering and missing out on plans one way or another. I also took the time to offer my help to volunteer and collected prescriptions for some of the elderly people in the local area. It was truly beautiful to see communities coming together to help one another. The rivers were clear again, pollution had cleared of smog and the air was purer than it had ever been in many cities. Families were spending quality time together.

I found a lot of positives in being locked down as there's always a silver lining even in the darkest of situations. I truly felt for a lot of businesses, though, including the Ltd companies that seemed to get left out of financial support or the business owners who didn't fit neatly into the categories of financial support being offered. I counted myself lucky that I had a self-employed business and a Ltd company, plus we were a two-person household to bring in income. Peter's income wasn't affected at all, and I felt truly grateful for that.

I also decided once again to take a break from any thoughts of IVF and just focus on what I could control: reconnecting with Peter again and putting my energies into building a new business idea that I felt really passionate about. I was also blessed that I had my horse up the road and was able to ride in the field away from others in order to stay isolated. Peter and I worked from home anyway and I was able to move the rest of my clients online instead of having face-to-face meetings and interactions.

It was difficult not having any end in sight, and no news of when restrictions might be lifted on travel, because it wasn't just a case of waiting to hear when IVF treatment was allowed to start up again, it was also dependent on two different countries' rules on travel. I heard lots of stories of people who had to stop IVF treatment halfway through and that must've been devastating. I already found it difficult not being able to start treatment or move my embryos, let alone stop mid-cycle.

It was a difficult time all around, for everyone. After five months of getting through lockdown, the lockdown rules started to ease up. I kept an eye on travel restrictions for Greece being lifted. It was looking like Greece was permitting travel from the UK. Finally! This was amazing news. I immediately contacted the courier and they said they were monitoring the situation. It wasn't to be. A few days later it became clear that Greece was allowing other countries in but not the UK due to how high our Covid rates still were. This was disappointing, but what could you do?

Greece then decided to permit UK citizens to travel to Athens, so we got everything organised between the clinics and arranged a pick-up date with the courier *again*, got everything booked ready to go and got our hopes up *again*, only to find that Greece had shut down its travel from the UK *again*. It was to be like that a few more times, with everything being ready to go after travel had been allowed again. One time, after we had received the green light for everything to finally move, it turned out that the courier didn't get a response in time from the clinic in the UK for a pick-up time. We missed the slot and the embryos had to stay put even longer. It truly was frustrating, but that's IVF. In a nutshell, it's not only a numbers game, but it's also a waiting game full of frustrations that will certainly test your patience to the limit.

I just let everything go by this point and thought, it'll just happen when it's meant to; there's no point stressing over what you can't control. Once you've spent years waiting, what's another few more months? I had truly learnt the value of patience and the art of letting go. I put my focus into other things, put it all out of my mind when out of the blue came the call that everything had been greenlit to go again and was happening within the next few days. Finally! I thought, 'I'm not going to get my hopes up too much until I had the confirmation that they'd landed in Athens!'

I thought about the little embryos off on their first journey and prayed they'd be kept safe. I received the call from the courier company to say the embryos had landed safely and the courier transporting them was waiting in a coffee shop for the clinic to open to drop them off. I literally had visions of the embryos in their tank sitting on the table in the coffee shop while he was drinking coffee. I found it quite amusing! I then had confirmation that the clinic had received them an hour later and I was able to get excited again. I reckoned it had now been twelve months since my last IVF treatment and I felt ready in every sense.

Sadly, Peter didn't feel the same way, and we'd gone back to having tension around us. I didn't like bringing up the subject as it never went well and he seemed very disengaged in the whole process. I told him the news and that I wanted to get started with treatment the following month. He wanted to wait until the following year and didn't understand the rush when times were so uncertain right now with many countries going back into a second lockdown. He had a point, but who knew what the following year would be like either? I believed the whole Covid situation was going to be here for a while.

We never seemed to reach an agreement but I was dead set on going for it anyway as there was no way I could wait another six months to start. Covid or not, I was going to do this IVF cycle and not even a deadly virus was going to put a stop to it finally going ahead. I figured once we were in Athens and the process had started then things would work out okay and he'd be on board with it.

It was to be agreed with the clinic that I'd do a natural cycle which meant no down-regulating, shutting off the hormones and boosting them again. It would be a case of lots of monitoring and being prescribed meds if and when needed. I chose a natural cycle as I didn't like the side effects from the drugs, and if the clinic offered it as an option and they had had great results then I trusted their judgment. Plus, I felt so sick from the first stimulated IVF cycle. This was to be it. All or nothing. Literally putting all our eggs into one basket so to speak! I knew it was a huge risk, but it was a risk I was willing to take. This was to be THE cycle.

TWENTY-SIX
A Greek Divorce!

'I Do, I Did, I'm Done!'

Our apartment was booked, right next to the clinic this time. Only five minutes' walk away. Bags packed, flights sorted. Everything had finally come together. I booked a flight that would get me in on Friday and Peter the following day as he had to work. He was excited about going to Athens as he hadn't been before, and I was glad he was looking forward to it and that we'd be there together this time. We all wore masks on the plane which was half empty so very nice.

It was so hot in Greece during September. I was pretty tired from travelling but glad to finally arrive at the apartment, although the name tags at the entrance of the apartment were in Greek, so I had no clue which one was mine. I rang the owner who spoke good English but, while we were talking, someone came to the door to let me in and show me around. The apartment wasn't exactly what I had been expecting and looked very different from the pictures, with a dark, dingy feel to it and the smell of musty, stale smoke lingering in the air. There was a small kitchen with the very basics, a small lounge and one bedroom with a painted picture of a half-naked woman on the wall! Tits...exactly what I wanted to wake up to each morning when I opened my eyes. (Sarcastic tone, rolling my eyes!)

Anyway, I was shattered and hungry and it was dark by this point. I ventured out and ended up wandering round and round the streets in a circle, making no decisions on food. Eventually I settled on the local supermarket.

Back in the apartment, I soon passed out until I was rudely awoken by a horrendous noise which sounded like machinery right outside my window. I checked the time...6 a.m. I looked out the window and saw workers digging up the road. Are you serious? 6 a.m. on a Saturday. Come on! There was no way of falling back to sleep with noise that loud as it was only single-glazed windows.

I decided to just get up and go exploring. I was looking forward to Peter arriving later that evening. He didn't seem overly impressed with the apartment either, but we figured the location was good as it was so close to the clinic, and so we decided to just stick it out. We got a fairly early night that night as we were both shattered, then were awakened at the same time again the following morning. Peter couldn't believe how loud the machinery was and decided to record it.

We then began to try to start our working day as we both needed to work while we were out there but neither of us could log on to the internet, and when we did, it was unbelievably slow. It was impossible to work.

We figured enough was enough, so I called the booking agent to complain and thankfully he was understanding, asking when we'd want to leave. I said we'd leave in the morning, hoping we'd find somewhere in that short space of time. He agreed we could do that and confirmed we could get a full refund. Thank God for that. Not a great start to IVF treatment, but at least we could move, start again and get our money back for the remaining two and a half weeks we were staying.

We managed to find another apartment somewhere not far away which looked lovely, and hoped the pictures would match reality. A bit like dating websites, really. We breathed a sigh of relief once we'd booked and paid for it as it had been so stressful trying to find somewhere else at the last minute.

Of course, anyone going through IVF is always warned to avoid stress like the plague. I logged on to my email from my phone to discover a message from the agent we booked through saying the owner of the apartments didn't agree to the cancellation and we'd not be receiving any refund after all, despite being mis-sold the apartment. WHAT? We were fuming. That's not what was said on the phone call. Why, oh why, didn't

I get it in writing? I'm normally so meticulous about that sort of thing.

I called them immediately, but they refused to acknowledge what had been agreed previously, and claimed that they didn't have a recording of the conversation, and so it was basically my word against theirs. We lost hundreds of pounds. It was a difficult pill to swallow, but we figured we just wanted out of the apartment. There was no way we could work from there and the noise in the morning was unbearable.

The minute we arrived in the new apartment, it was like a breath of fresh air. There was an open plan kitchen, dining room and living room leading out onto a balcony with an outside table and two bedrooms with really good air conditioning.

I loved the outside shutters that made the rooms pitch black to sleep in. It was lovely and bright too. We instantly relaxed and spent our days working and chilling at the apartment along with cooking meals and eating on the balcony in the hot sun. Bliss! Just for that reason alone, it was worth having IVF abroad!

We visited the acropolis as Peter hadn't seen it and had a couple of meals out too. We took a trip to the flea market and just enjoyed a relaxed pace of life. This is what I loved about Greece: the food, the beautiful scenery and the history. Then it was back to business—time to get on the IVF cycle again!

TWENTY-SEVEN
Third and Last Round IVF

*'If you want a rainbow you have
to put up with the rain'*

Peter and I both needed to have blood tests done at the clinic to check for STDs, which is standard when embarking on an IVF cycle, and they needed to be done within the last three months. As the clinic had strict rules about anybody visiting during times of Covid, they arranged for a nurse to travel to our apartment to take our Covid tests. We weren't allowed to go to the clinic without a negative result first which, fortunately, we passed.

We had daily visits to the clinic for me to be monitored during my cycle as I had ovulated two days after arriving—which the clinic then confirmed. The consultant said everything looked great, my womb lining was thick, and they planned to have the transfer done six days later. It was very exciting, although I was nervous about the outcome as we'd put in so much time, effort and money into this. Hopefully this time, the risks would pay off. We were given Ovitrelle, which was an hCG booster, which helped boost implantation which I needed to take a few days before embryo transfer and I had two injections to take beforehand, a day or two apart. I also had my hormones checked before transfer to check progesterone levels—they seemed good.

On the day of transfer, I was feeling particularly nervous. We were told to come in at midday but an hour before we were due, I was becoming more and more panicked about the thawing process. I don't know why because I'd never been concerned about it before. I was so nervous that something would go wrong. I had nothing to comfort me as I hadn't been told in advance what the process would be.

I spoke to my mum and explained I was feeling particularly nervous and that, for some reason, I was feeling concerned about my embryos not thawing correctly. I sounded so worried that my mum took the decision to ring the clinic without telling me, to inform them that I was very nervous and to make sure I was relaxed and looked after. I didn't find out until we arrived at the clinic that she'd spoken to them. I was so embarrassed! I didn't expect her to say anything. The whole day the doctors made sure to tell me not to be nervous, that stress wasn't good for implantation, etc. The embarrassment of it all made me on edge.

The doctor talked us through the procedure and explained they would do a scan first to check everything was good and to check that the embryos had thawed.

Then they would proceed with the transfer. She seemed very positive and upbeat about the whole thing and told us to send her a picture of the baby in nine months. She had such a flamboyant personality, which was refreshing because a lot of IVF doctors could be cold, direct and stony-faced. I needed a bit of warmth, compassion and empathy with a bit of humour thrown in to help me cope.

We put on our plastic shoe coverings and hats and waited in a cubicle to be called. Luckily, Peter was allowed to be in the room to witness the transfer because many partners weren't allowed due to Covid restrictions. Perhaps my mum telling them how nervous I was did help in the end!

It turned out that my fears weren't unfounded after all. The embryologist came in to tell us that one of the embryos was doing well after the thawing process and seemed really strong, but the other hadn't survived and had died. That was devastating news to hear and to go into transfer with that on our shoulders. We'd spent so much of the holiday joking about how we'd cope with twins. Needing to buy two sets of everything and which baby you'd pick up first if both were crying. But secretly liking the idea of it.

It wasn't to be, though, and I felt bad for the poor little embryo. I liked the idea of having both embryos transferred. I guess only the strongest survive. I figured if the other little mite survived travelling across Europe and a plane ride, it was definitely a strong contender to make it through the whole nine months.

We needed to put our hopes into the embryo which would be transferred. I know the news of the other embryo hit Peter quite hard and he was quite down about it. Finally, it was our time for transfer. We walked into the transfer room, and I got into position on the gurney. There seemed to be around five people around me made up of assistant nurses, etc., which was a bit unnerving, but Dr Athanasia soon made us feel at ease.

No sooner was I lying down, trying to get as relaxed as I could, when suddenly I looked up to see a huge METAL speculum in between my legs! You're seriously not putting THAT inside me, are you? Yep, very serious. In it went, ouch! I kept being told to relax but it was hard to with metal clamps inside me.

At least the process was over with quickly and I watched the embryo being placed into my womb. Just like that! As soon as it started it was over! That's the thing with a transfer, you build yourself up so much for hours then *pfft*! It's done and you're PUPO! Pregnant until proven otherwise!

I was told to stay lying down for thirty minutes to help implantation. Peter and I were left alone and we discussed the day's events and the poor embryo that didn't make it. Once we were ready to leave, we went down to reception to settle up and pay—almost like going into a shop. Buying a baby and going to the till to pay for it! This is when we had the shock of our lives! It was double the cost of what we'd expected. I hadn't budgeted in my finances for that. It was beyond what I'd saved! We were shocked and livid—which wasn't great for implantation.

Apparently you pay per straw. We didn't realise this at the time, but we had two embryos which meant two straws—which meant double the cost. This wasn't made at all clear at the beginning of the whole process. This soon brought costs with everything else around the £3,000 mark. Peter covered the other half and we got a lift back by the clinic's driver. We were not happy, especially when we didn't have the other embryo transferred but still paid the same cost. Not a great start for the two-week wait to begin.

Peter struggled to shake it off, but I told him to imagine if neither embryo survived the thawing process and we had nothing to transfer, yet we still had to pay for both. There's always a worse situation to be in and we needed to be grateful for the embryo that did make it as not everyone is blessed with that. I was generally the one who always tried to see the positive side and the best scenario which balanced us out as a couple.

Peter always expected the worst but hoped for the best and looked at all the scenarios that could go wrong so that he could prepare himself. We were quite sub-dued the rest of the evening, but I spent the time talking to the embryo and welcoming him/her into their new world and told him/her or whatever it wanted to be to make themselves at home.

TWENTY-EIGHT
2WW

'The 2WW Must Be In Dog Time, because It Feels More Like A Year Than 14 Days'

We were sad but ready to come home as we'd been away for two and a half weeks... but it was definitely difficult to come back to dark, wet, dreary weather. Why is it always raining when you land in London after being in a hot country?

I did worry if travelling on a plane was safe with an embryo on board, but was advised it was okay to do so. We landed really late and I was beyond exhausted but was excited the next day to see my cat and horse. Not both in the house—obviously. Although that would be pretty cool! I carried on working, trying to keep my mind off testing as I didn't want to test too early and get a false negative. All members of the secret fertility club know what I mean!

My emotions were swinging from being super positive, confident everything would work out to a few hours later full of fear, despair, helplessness and sheer panic.

What if it hasn't worked?

What if we've spent all our money and used all our embryos with no result?

What will we do if it's failed?'

I needed something to keep my mind off the possible result as the clinic had also emphasised that it was very important not to be stressed. Which, of course, created more stress! It was a vicious circle. I tried to rationalise with myself, 'Well, I've had the ectopics, the miscarriage and the failed cycle, so the chances of a repeat surely out of all the embryos are slim as I'm definitely due some good luck this time.'

Some days the fear was debilitating as we'd invested literally everything into this and some days I felt as though I was having a panic attack. My heart would beat through my chest and my hands would be shaking. I wasn't sleeping much as my mind went through 'what ifs' at a million miles per hour. I don't know why we put ourselves through it. Not that we have much control over it, which is why you want to punch someone in the face when they say, 'Just relax. It will be okay. It will work out this time I can feel it!' Grrr, okay, punching is a bit harsh, just a ninja-style fly kick!

I started listening to affirmations twice a day to help stay positive and keep me relaxed, and I used visualisations to create an image of everything developing as it should. But really, in the end, it's all down to Mother Nature and we have no control over how it will work out apart from our commitment to look after ourselves.

I'm sure in a perfect world—where you're able to happily try IVF as many times as you wish, have the skin of a rhino so negative results wouldn't affect you at all, all the money in the world, no arguments with partners whatsoever and the technology that ensures every embryo turns out perfectly with conditions being perfect every time to develop the pregnancy to full term with absolutely no problems—it will feel like a stress-free experience. We dare to dream.

Perhaps in twenty years' time, IVF will be completely different from the way it is now. I bet when they first announced the invention of IVF, people were gobsmacked at the thought that it could ever exist and possibly believed it would never work. Maybe something else will come along as technology continues to advance that will help millions more achieve their dream.

TWENTY-NINE
Pregnant and Nervous!

'It Always Seems Impossible Until It's Done'

I woke up early on the day we were allowed to test. I had barely slept and really wanted to get the panic over with as I was having severe anxiety about the result, ranging from needing to know ASAP through to not wanting to know at all and preferring to bury my head in the sand. I knew so much was riding on this, which made the result so much more of a gamble and the pressure was nearly becoming too much to take.

It was 6 a.m. and I grabbed the tests and headed to the bathroom with Peter still asleep. I peed on the stick and checked it after a minute, only one line—that meant it was negative. My heart was literally in my mouth. I grabbed the packet instructions from the other room with an overwhelming sense of doom washing over me, already trying to figure out how to not only tell Peter the sad news but also everyone else as well. It was almost too much to bear. The instructions confirmed my worst fears. I was devastated. I decided to head back into the bathroom and give the test one last look and nearly fell over from the shock! Two lines—PREGNANT!!

I rushed into the bedroom and woke Peter up shouting from the top of my lungs, 'I'm pregnant! It's positive!' He seemed really happy and looked at the test I was still holding in my hand. I was still physically shaking but beyond happy. Nothing could get me down from this cloud I was on. Phew, I could breathe as all that time, effort and investment into treatment had paid off after all. I quickly began messaging all my friends and family. Who cared it was only 7 a.m? They needed to know!

After my third blood test, my hCG levels had increased from 120 to 1433ml in a week! My clinic was a bit concerned at first as my hCG levels had been really low. This can indicate a potential problem early on with the pregnancy, but they prescribed me an hCG booster, which helps to boost the pregnancy level of hCG and improves the pregnancy outcome.

They also put me on daily Clexane, which is a blood thinner, to help prevent miscarriage. My progesterone doubled from 31 to 70 which was good, but it was still early days. I was also taking low dose progesterone supplements. Whilst awaiting the results of my third blood test to show if my hCG levels were increasing or declining, I saw the email come through from the local clinic and became really nervous.

My heart was pounding hard as I was terrified of what the results would say. I know every pregnancy is different and develops at its own pace, but I was so worried that the numbers might have dropped or weren't progressing, which can sometimes signify a problem or can lead to either miscarriage or failure to develop. On the other hand though, there are many times when it just needs to play catch up, like in this case.

I shouted loudly up the stairs for my partner to come down and look too. I messaged my friend the results and she was literally sobbing with happiness when she read them. She'd been on the edge of her seat, waiting as nervously as I was. I was so happy that things were looking promising.

Most people who conceive naturally, and don't need to undergo fertility treatment, wouldn't even know what their hCG levels would be at this stage—which can be a blessing in disguise. Either way, when you have had struggles—which I'm sure a lot of you who are reading this book have, not to mention your fair share of battles to overcome—I'm sure you'll agree with me that you need to celebrate the small wins and each and every small milestone.

The next milestone was the viability scan, which determines if there is an embryo growing and if the pregnancy is deemed 'viable'. Now just as I'd been able to breathe a sigh of relief again, I had to jump right back on the rollercoaster of holding my breath until I was (fingers crossed), past that hurdle too.

The time soon came round for the first scan and I felt like I was waiting for a courtroom verdict for a life sentence. It can feel very isolating on this journey, especially waiting for each scan and each milestone of early pregnancy, despite having an outpouring of love from those close to you. I'd been awake since 6 a.m. and all week I'd been waking up consistently at 3 a.m. and 5 a.m. with stressful dreams. I'm not sure if it was down to the meds I was taking, the pregnancy or my worries—perhaps all three. I spent the night before the first scan trying to keep busy with work as much as I could. Normally on the morning of these appointments, I'd keep myself busy with clients, but I couldn't face it as I knew my mind wouldn't be focused.

I awoke panicked as I didn't feel any cramping, although my breasts were still sore. Symptoms did seem to come and go; I'd barely had any nausea or sickness. I tried to put my mind at rest by telling myself every pregnancy is different and not everyone is going to feel or be sick. I took myself downstairs on the day of the scan at 6 a.m. with my mind racing with thoughts at 100 million miles per hour. I had been googling constantly (I know, I know!).

What are the chances of a second missed miscarriage in a row? (2% actually.)

How to prepare mentally for the first scan.

Six ways to beat pregnancy anxiety.

Anxiety before ultrasound.

How to deal with first scan nerves.

Seven-week cramping disappeared.

Seven weeks not tired anymore.

You get the gist. My mood swings ranged from thinking up every possible scan scenario from: what my nerves would be like being told there's no heartbeat and seeing the sad look on the nurse's face as she delivered the news, through to actually panicking that there wouldn't be a baby in there at all.—I know, it's crazy what our minds can concoct. When I'd finished panicking over those things, I started panicking over what would happen if we were told some awful news about something we hadn't prepared for or even considered. It's what had always happened previously, so I felt it was bound to happen again.

Every day, when pregnant again after suffering loss, I had a constant nagging feeling of dread, and no matter how much I pottered around the house, messaged my friends, reassured myself, listened to reassurance from others, nothing settled the constant spiral of thoughts and possible scenarios inside my head. I would then worry about worrying and the stress it might be putting on the baby. It was a vicious circle. There were still a few hours until the scan appointment, and so I decided to put on my 'first-trimester' fertility affirmations while my partner was still asleep upstairs. My cat came to join me as I repeated the positive affirmations out loud, convincing myself and trying to visualise receiving good news, imagining that I could see the baby straight away and see the little heartbeat flicker on the monitor and reminded myself of the facts that

❖ My levels had jumped from 120 u/l to 1433 u/l in over a week

❖ Symptoms would come and go, it's normal

❖ The chances of something going wrong again are low

❖ There are many positive stories of success of women who have gone on to have completely normal pregnancies after loss through to full term and why wouldn't that be me too?

❖ No matter the outcome, I have supportive people around me and will get through it

❖ I cannot change, control or determine the outcome of any stage

I had found writing my feelings down on paper the most therapeutic and the best form of getting control over the negative, intrusive thoughts and feelings I felt. I opted for a private scan because I hadn't heard anything back about being referred for an NHS scan (I'm meant to be scanned at six weeks due to my previous history). I was now seven weeks + one day. I also wasn't allowed anyone with me at the scan with the NHS due to Covid rates. I understand why but it's very harsh to have to hear bad news about pregnancy on your own, I already knew how that felt and it wasn't nice at all. It was worth paying extra for a private scan to have the extra support no matter the outcome. The waiting was the hardest part, for sure. I was in no man's land.

THIRTY
'Hello Bad News, I've Been Expecting You'

'Already In My Heart, Someday In My Arms'

I had full-on anxiety in the car driving to the scan centre. It was a thirty-minute drive and luckily Peter did the driving. He was chatting to me about work on the way but I wasn't able to focus on anything he was saying. I was desperately trying to quell the butterflies in my tummy and stop my mind racing through all the possible outcomes.

I was absolutely dreading it and felt like a prisoner awaiting a death verdict. Peter asked me how I was feeling, and I responded that I was very nervous and didn't really want to discuss it as I knew it wouldn't help me. He assured me everything would be fine and not to get anxious as there were many scans to go and stress could also affect the baby. I knew this but I had tried literally EVERYTHING to try and control it. It's never obvious to anyone else when I'm experiencing panic unless they know me well. I just go very silent and distant whilst battling with my inner turmoil.

We walked into the clinic wearing our face masks, filled out some forms about previous history, which was the last thing I wanted to focus on, then sat down waiting. Waiting rooms are terrible places, especially waiting rooms for scans. Everyone in the Fertility Club knows exactly what I mean. A couple came out of the scanning room excited and happy as they sat down opposite us.

Must be their first scan, I thought a little sourly. They looked like newbies and I doubted that they'd had to deal with any previous issues and probably it was a natural pregnancy. Funny how we sum people up and make assumptions. A receptionist came over and showed them their scan-pictures and pointed to their due date. I felt happy for them, albeit a little jealous and bitter and even more scared of what our fate would be. The receptionist congratulated them as they left the scanning centre then called us in and asked us if we were ready. 'Not really' I replied.

I walked into the scanning room with Peter and looked to the left to see a male sonographer sitting at the machine. I was now petrified. Peter and I quickly glanced at each other in horror. I had never been scanned by a male before. I understand there are very competent male sonographers, and we live in an equal world (for the most part minus equal pay and other things I won't go into). BUT I hadn't been warned my sonographer would be male, and felt I had been put in an uncomfortable situation when I was already very, very nervous. Typical, I thought. I know exactly how this is going to play out, I can just feel it.

His female assistant asked me to go behind the curtain and remove my bottom clothes and wrap myself with a paper towel. I was normally fine with this process as I had been scanned many, many times before, but today I wanted to be anywhere but in the room.

I did what they asked and laid myself onto the bed, ready to be scanned internally. My breathing was getting quicker and quicker and I could feel myself almost going into a full-blown, uncontrollable panicked frenzy! I looked worriedly at Peter, who was at my side then tried to focus on my breathing. I kept repeating over and over in my mind, 'No matter the outcome, you can handle this.'

I knew immediately something wasn't right. Call it intuition or whatever but I've done enough scans now to know when there's a problem. The sonographer went quiet and took a while to give me any updates. Both he and the assistant were staring at the screen as I heard clicking sounds from the mouse which sounded amplified through a silence filled with tension. Normally, if things were fine, they'd talk to me and give me reassurance and feedback straight away—in my experience anyway. I'm not saying that it's textbook, though. I quickly prepared myself as much as I could do for the outcome. The sonographer asked us when the transfer was, but I couldn't think; my mind went completely blank. I frantically asked Peter, but he didn't know either. Then it came back to me, 'Twenty-sixth September,' I replied, which would've made me seven weeks four days.

He went on to explain, 'I've had a thorough look on both sides on your womb and I can only see a pocket of fluid, but nothing else.' He proceeded to show me the screen. 'At this stage, we expect to see a yolk sac and foetal pole, but we're only seeing the gestational sac, which shows the start of pregnancy but no embryo.' My heart dropped completely. Hello bad news, we've been here before. Many times. He went on to say that they diagnose this as a 'pregnancy in an unknown location'. This can mean a number of outcomes:

A. It's too early and the dates don't align (which is rare as IVF dates are very accurate)

B. Ectopic pregnancy (he ruled this out and said it was extremely unlikely as he had checked and couldn't see evidence of that and with IVF they place it in the womb)

C. An impending miscarriage where the pregnancy fails to develop. Not again!

I didn't cry. We tried to take the information in as the assistant told us she was ringing our local hospital to refer us to the Early Pregnancy Unit. (Been there a few times.). She gave us a leaflet to take away. They both left the room. I got dressed then Peter and I sat on the sofa. We just felt so confused as there was no definite diagnosis. We were told, 'Well, it could be a number of things.' Either way, it didn't look good. We were deflated. Seriously? How can we be back here again?

The assistant came back in to tell me to do another pregnancy test in the morning and, if positive, to call back and they'd arrange for me to go to the Early Pregnancy Unit at the hospital. She asked if we wanted to leave out of the back exit so we wouldn't have to do what felt like the walk of shame, past all the excited, hopeful couples who probably had a whole pregnancy ahead of them. We swiftly agreed and left.

The drive home felt full of confusion and complete numbness along with physical exhaustion from the mental torture I'd put myself through waiting on the outcome. In some respects, I was just glad it was over so I had some idea of what I was dealing with. Waiting for the first scan to arrive was the hardest part for me. Peter began trying to reassure me by saying, 'None of this is our fault. We did everything exactly as we were supposed to. No matter what happened, we couldn't have prevented any of it. You're amazing for having put yourself through it all again.' They were really kind words, but I just couldn't absorb them at this point. I was also not willing to accept the diagnosis that it hadn't worked.

Once we arrived home, I knew I just needed to get out of the house. Peter asked me if there was anything he could do, but there wasn't really anything anybody could do. I just needed to see my best friend Jess who always was there in these moments of bad news and always knew what to say. She was always a great listener too.

We went to the local café, and by this point, I was starving as my hunger returned with a vengeance after the fight-or-flight mode had disappeared. We chatted over tea and cake as I poured my heart out from the diagnosis and my fears for the future. 'What if it doesn't work? We've spent so much money and time preparing for this.

It was so hard to get Peter on board this time, after all our previous losses, that I think he's reached his limit. What if this keeps happening that we never have a baby? What then? How many times can we keep putting ourselves through this at a risk to ourselves and our relationship? Spending thousands on it and never being able to own a house as all the money is spent on trying to achieve this dream?'

She had tears in her eyes and so did I as the reality hit once again, of not only the potential loss of another baby and the hopes and dreams alongside it, but real fears for my relationship and the future. I felt even more confused as I was starting to really process the information. She reassured me: 'Look, you don't have all the results yet. Let's see what the hospital says when you go for your scan. It could just be very early, and perhaps the embryo hadn't shown up on the scan yet.'

Yes, I still had some hope left but I was also realistic. I told her about needing to do the pregnancy test in the morning and we both decided it would be better to do it with her being around for support. We agreed to pick one up from the supermarket and do the test in the toilet. Classy! As we left the café, we walked past a group of new mothers and their babies—typical! Always the way, when you receive bad news about your own pregnancy the worst part is having it rubbed in your face. Thanks, universe!

We bought the test, and I felt like a sixteen-year-old that didn't want my family to find out I was pregnant as I crammed into a tiny supermarket toilet trying to pee on a stick. God, they spend so many years in school trying to prevent us from falling pregnant but never told us the flip side of the coin—the cold fact of how bloody difficult it can also be. I nervously waited for the stick to show me the result as if I was doing it for the first time all over again.

Two lines appeared! Pregnant! I was relieved and gave Jess a massive hug outside. Perhaps there was still hope after all. I went home that evening and began googling 'pregnancy of an unknown location,' and 'gestational sac, no embryo positive stories'. I read a few success stories where the embryo had not shown up on the first scan but had appeared on the second one. Another anecdote told of a girl who was advised to terminate after a pregnancy failed to progress, but after waiting a few weeks to decide, a scan revealed an embryo and heartbeat.

But for the few stories of success—which mostly turned out to be natural pregnancies where the dates weren't aligned—there were plenty of negative, unsuccessful ones.

I decided to post in a group that was part of my IVF clinic about my recent diagnosis and received a lot of love from my fertility warriors, along with a reality check. No-one who had experienced this scenario had had a positive result. Perhaps I'd just been in denial and needed to face facts. But I was exhausted. I decided sleep was the best thing at that moment just for the chance to escape for a while.

THIRTY-ONE
More testing

*'Sometimes it's hard to see a rainbow when
there's been endless days of rain'*

I felt better in the morning when I awoke after a restful
night's sleep, the first in a long time. I had completely
worn myself out with all the worry, but now felt calm
and ready to face whatever news I'd be told at the Early
Pregnancy Unit. It wasn't nice having to revisit there as
all my surgeries and ectopic pregnancies happened in
that place, not to mention that the heartbreak of being
dismissed from my previous ectopic was still fresh in my
mind. But I needed to know the outcome of this. Peter
felt the same as I did. Neither of us really didn't want to
go back there as we didn't have a single good memory.

Our appointment was very early in the morning at
the weekend, and due to Covid, Peter wasn't allowed in
the scanning room with me. I sat in the waiting room
alongside other ladies who were waiting to be seen.
All of them seemed very nervous and I really felt for
them, knowing how I had the rollercoaster of emotions

I had felt the day before. I really wish we were more open, like the Americans, and spoke to each other a bit more, especially in these waiting rooms. I bet if we just reached out and shared each other's stories we'd be able to comfort one another instead of actively trying to not catch each other's eye like we're travelling on the Tube. I wondered what they were here for and what their story was, and if it was their first time. You only come to the Early Pregnancy Unit if there is a potential issue with your pregnancy or if you have had a previous history of loss or risk and need to be closely monitored.

I was seen after half an hour and first had a consultation then was told there would be a long wait as it was the weekend. I'd have a scan then bloods taken to determine what my hormones and pregnancy hCG level was to figure out what was going on. At least I didn't have to pay, for once. Monitoring my blood tests privately had been costing me £100.

I waited what seemed like hours then was called in for the scan. The sonographer was there and also her assistant nurse. They were lovely. She did a tummy and internal scan, but the results were still the same—'pocket of fluid'. I asked her what the outcomes generally were with this, and she replied, 'It really varies. It can go either way.' Thanks, very helpful. They probably don't like to give away too much. I had to then have my bloods done, a full blood count and hCG, and was told I needed to wait to get results which would take a few hours. I might also require a laparoscopy later to try and find the pregnancy. WHAT? I didn't know I'd be coming in for surgery!

All the while I was getting scanned and receiving bad news, Peter was spending the whole day in the café downstairs waiting. Once I had my blood test done, I was told to wait back in the waiting room. By this point the six girls, who had been there too, had come and gone, but there was another girl crying with a nurse consoling her.

My heart really went out to her, I knew exactly what place she was in and knew how devastating it was to hear bad news. Although it was still hard to hear, I had heard it enough to build a bit more resilience to it whatever the outcome. I really wanted to help her, but I also knew there was nothing I could say that would help make things any better. Only time could do that. My full blood count came back normal, but I was told that they'd need to ring me with the hCG result later that day. The doctor said, although she'd seen cases go against the textbook, it also didn't look great at this stage. Yes, I'm aware, thanks for pointing it out to me again.

Peter and I went home. I really didn't know what to do with myself with all these unresolved emotions floating around in my mind. We bought some junk food and watched trashy telly. We'd stopped drinking a few months ago before treatment started and technically, I was still 'pregnant', 'half pregnant', whatever you wanted to call it. Until we had complete evidence it was over, I still needed to act responsibly and take the IVF meds.

It was Halloween so we watched 'Psycho' waiting for the doctor to call to let me know the outcome of my hCG, and if it was showing the levels dropping or something similar (which tended to mean the pregnancy was not developing any more and a miscarriage was on its way). I'd had no bleeding, so my body was carrying on as if it were still pregnant, but apparently you don't always need bleeding to have a miscarriage. I was definitely aware of that from my previous silent miscarriage. I went up to bed early and Peter decided to work. That was his way of dealing with things, but I just needed time alone to process things and it was starting to hit home again.

The doctor didn't phone at all, which was really shitty, leaving me in limbo without any clue as to the outcome of an impending pregnancy. But what could I do? God, it takes a warrior to repeatedly put yourself in these situations and come out of it each time still half normal and sane. I lay in bed thinking about the uncertainty of my future hanging in the balance and the reality of it all started to sink in. I always believed that every cycle would be the one that would work. I told myself, 'This one is it. I can feel it.' Everyone around me felt it too. It's a time of such hope and positivity that I didn't mind injecting myself every day with drugs. I felt strongly that I would get something out of it, something worthwhile putting myself through the mental torture.

But when it crashed down around me, taking me back to square one, it took a piece of my heart with it too. I came out of it a little different as a person. I kept asking myself, 'How many times can you keep putting yourself through this?' I mean, I'm a pretty strong person. I've been through a lot of shit, but everyone has a limit. It really is a battle of perseverance and mental strength, but also a gamble on losing everything in the process—my relationship, finances, my sanity. It comes at a cost. I asked myself, 'When is enough, enough?'

THIRTY-TWO
The MIA pregnancy

*'There is no greater agony than bear-
ing an untold story inside of you'*

I finally heard from the doctor. She called and she asked
me how I was feeling. I said, 'Very tired, but open to hearing whatever it is you need to tell me as I've mentally
prepared myself.'

'Well,' she replied, 'That's the thing. We got your
results back for your hCG and they're at 21,000 and
your progesterone 104.' She said, in her ten-years' experience, she'd never dealt with a case as difficult as this
and found it completely baffling.

I was told to come in the next day. They were bringing in the most advanced sonographer in the whole of
south UK, who had the expertise to deal with the most
difficult cases. She also asked if I had had two embryos
transferred with IVF. I explained, 'No, just one. The
other didn't make it during the thawing process.'

She said, 'Normally, I'd see these numbers with
twins. An embryo could've split in two, but we'd expect

to see something. It could be perhaps an ectopic migration somewhere in the abdomen. Or it might be that it needed to reach a peak before levels started dropping and a miscarriage would then ensue'.

She explained I'd also need perhaps an MRI scan or laparoscopy. I just didn't want to go through another ectopic—my third! All I wanted was for the doctors to turn around and say, 'Oh look, we see your embryo here. It's very small but in the right place.' But in reality...

It was also difficult as I had started thinking of myself as not pregnant any more, only to then have a spanner thrown in the works. I held on desperately to a tiny glimmer of hope that things would work out.

I went in for another scan a few days later which didn't show any signs of development, so I was told to come back a week later for a scan as my hCG had gone up another 16% but my progesterone had gone down slightly. Meanwhile, my body was still holding on to the pregnancy and giving all the symptoms such as food aversions—this time to bacon rashers. I couldn't even look at a packet without feeling nauseous.

Every day I had extreme fatigue. Most of my work had to be pushed aside, which was difficult, as I was in the middle of a single release for one of my artists. We had a full PR campaign behind it and lots of social media coverage was needed on a regular basis from my end. The world doesn't stop spinning just because sometimes you want it to.

I tried to push the majority of my work aside while I awaited the news of the outcome, at least with the other pregnancies a decision was made quickly so there was no waiting on 'what ifs' and prolonging the hurtful emotions if it wasn't to be. My friends and family were checking in regularly and were hanging on a cliff's edge for an answer as much as Peter and me.

I felt a sense of being removed from my daily life, stuck in limbo without being able to get closure or remain hopeful as the doctors and stats weren't on our side. Some days I wasted watching endless Netflix films to take a break from my work and to help take my mind off it all. But it only got me thinking more when I wasn't busy, so I decided throwing myself into work was the best thing to do.

I also started getting shooting pains from my right temple, like a migraine and pains in my left side similar to the start of an ectopic. I was out for dinner one night with my family and could barely eat from a constant nagging pain in my side and exhaustion at a level I'd never known.

I didn't want to make a fuss, so I tried to pretend all was okay. Ectopic had recently been ruled out so it wasn't that. But once you've had an ectopic, the pains never leave you in the sense that when anything happens that slightly resembles the familiar sensations, it sends your mind into a panic. Fortunately, I awoke the next day and the symptoms had dispersed. I also decided during this waiting time, as I eagerly awaited my verdict on the pregnancy, that I would try to stay positive and write a list of all the things I could do not being pregnant:

Fun Things To Do Not Being Pregnant:

❖ Drink wine at Xmas and get way drunker than I should!

❖ Ride my horse as often as I like

❖ Plan a fun shopping trip to Paris on Eurostar with Jess

❖ Book a cabin in snowy mountains with Peter (once this virus buggers off)

❖ Eat all the foods you can't have when pregnant like camembert, Pâté, sushi, medium cooked steaks, fish, meats like salami, junk food in general

❖ As many cups of tea as I like in a day

- ❖ Book a spa day with massages and full-on pampering

These are just a few that I know give me something to look forward to and have previously helped me through each loss. They may also help if anyone is in a similar situation at the moment, but only when and if you feel up to it. I know sometimes moving beyond a loss isn't easy. But these things helped me so perhaps they can also help you?

I was mentally preparing for the worst but hoping for the best and was finding some days easier than others. My friends were a lot more hopeful than I was at this stage. Some days I was so fatigued I couldn't even move from the sofa all day, which I put down to the hCG pregnancy symptoms my body was still experiencing. Normally I'm a 'can't sit still, always on the go' kind of person, so it was quite hard to adjust to.

My clinic told me to continue the IVF meds until there was a definitive outcome. My social media profile looked as though everything was normal, hunky-dory: that work was going well and life was great.

It's the reason I never allow myself to be influenced by people's profiles as they only ever post their 'best life'. It's just not real at all. I never post about my personal life as Peter and I are normally very much secret squirrels. This is the reason why this book is even more special for me. I'm sharing a piece of myself—my innermost vulnerabilities and hurts—to help others through this lonely, difficult journey and to unite us together, rather than leaving fertility warriors to battle it all alone.

THIRTY-THREE
When Life Throws You Lemons...

'Grab the salt and tequila'

The evening before the final scan, I was very nervous. On top of everything else, I also had a logistical nightmare. Peter had to work and was covering for others who were off so he was only able to drop me at the hospital, and wouldn't be able to pick me up until he finished at 6 p.m. I really didn't want to hang around as hospitals aren't the most enjoyable places to be left in. Also, I reckoned, if it was bad news then I needed someone to be there to support me. I felt in my gut that this was how the day would go and didn't envision a positive result from the scan.

Either way, I just needed a resolution once and for all as I really didn't want it to be dragged out any longer than it needed to. Luckily, I had a few offers from friends and family to assist and my friend Jess stepped in, which I was grateful for.

I barely slept a wink that night and felt exhausted once the morning came around. I was in a fight/flight mode the moment I woke up, feeling on edge and dazed. I didn't have to wait too long to be seen by a consultant who explained how the day would go and asked me how I was feeling, what my symptoms were, etc. I'd still had no bleeding by this point but had a lot of cramping and still complete exhaustion.

Things were tense at home too. Peter was throwing himself into his work as he was working two jobs, so he didn't have much time for anything outside of that, and I was feeling increasingly alone. I've never been one to talk easily about my feelings and neither was he, which didn't help. We each have our own coping mechanisms and ours were shutting down and shutting off. A lot of my friends and family messaged me wishing me luck, and I felt the added pressure of being the bearer of bad news if it didn't go well.

An Indian lady, who came across as very direct and professional, and had an air of superiority about her, introduced herself and explained that she would be doing my scan. It seemed she was the top of the chain in the world of sonographers. Many of the other nurses in the gynaecology department looked up to her, so I felt in good hands. I could tell instantly, after having become a bit of an expert in scanning techniques, that she was a cut above the rest. She seemed very thorough, pressing down on my tummy to reach different locations in my womb to get a clear indication of what was going on.

Afterwards, she said in a matter-of-fact way, 'I'm sorry, but there are no developments since your last scan. It seems like it hasn't developed beyond a gestational sac.' In truth, at least medically speaking, the pregnancy hadn't even evolved to the foetus stage. I had the sac but nothing else.

So, while my body went through all the pregnancy symptoms, the problem was that the foetus itself was missing. In my mind, I had still been pregnant at least for a short time, but I accepted it and told her I was expecting the news anyway and was pretty much used to hearing disappointing news by this point. I felt pretty numb to it all, quite frankly.

She explained that the consultant would go through options with me. I already knew what those options were as I'd been through this with the silent miscarriage previously and told her I'd already made up my mind on that. At least there was some comfort in being prepared. It was definitely easier than being blindsided by news I wasn't really expecting and having the wind knocked out of my sails.

I was taken to a private room and joined by one of the consultants who seemed friendly and compassionate. She gave me lots of leaflets about the different options available for assisting the miscarriage. You have an option for a natural miscarriage, which happens when the body is ready and can apparently involve a lot of heavy bleeding and cramping similar to contractions. There's also a chance of seeing the pregnancy tissue and perhaps the embryo if the pregnancy was that far along.

Some women like to follow the natural route and find some form of comfort in seeing the process happen as a way of saying goodbye.

I knew I definitely didn't want that option as the cramping sounded painful and I didn't like the unpredictability of it potentially happening at any time. The second option is the medicated route, where they give you misoprostol (brand name: Cytotec) to help speed up the process and pregnancy tissue passes at home. This happens within a week rather than a few weeks in a natural miscarriage.

I didn't like the idea of taking medication or the idea that there could be a chance not everything would be removed, meaning I would need surgery to complete the procedure. I like to be in control of a situation as much as I'm able to, which is rare in IVF and fertility situations, so I have always opted for the surgery route, also known as D&C (dilation and curettage).

It's done under general anaesthetic and the surgeons would remove pregnancy tissue from my womb using a suction catheter which would be inserted vaginally and into the uterus. At this stage, some people get their embryos, etc., tested if there have been repeated miscarriages. But on the NHS, you need three consecutive miscarriages to qualify. It saddens me that in this day and age we accept the prognosis that miscarriage is just 'something that happens' and 'most of the time there's no explanation'. Science and technology are so advanced now that it is beyond my comprehension that we don't have more of understanding of this. More research needs to be done as people who have suffered losses deserve answers that could help them go on to have successful pregnancies.

I believe that the charity 'Tommy's', which specialises in pregnancy loss has started a petition to call for more research to be done on miscarriage, and to offer more answers for anyone who has suffered. For those of you who may go on to miscarry in the future, please do take the time to sign it if you feel more should be done on this.

The consultant gave me some information regarding a service that I would be able to attend which would be a communal one with others who had also lost their babies and would involve scattering the ashes together in their rainbow garden. I always decided against these ceremonies as it would be too emotional for me. I opted to do something personal in my own way, such as lighting a candle to honour the loss and my babies. I completely understand why many people would want to take part in the service to say goodbye, and anything that helps to heal is always a great thing.

I was then given a mountain of paperwork to fill out then taken down to the pre-op department for testing before surgery, which was booked in for a few days later. It took half the day but it passed in a daze. I found myself just staring out of the window completely numb to it all, having no clue what my future looked like or if I'd ever be wanting to potentially go through all this yet again.

Meanwhile, my friend Jess was waiting downstairs in the café the whole time for me. Everything to do with fertility and pregnancy was made that much harder with Covid around, but at least we were able to navigate our way through it together. Once it was over at the hospital, Jess drove me home and I felt I wanted to be anywhere but there. It felt such a cold, lonely place to me for some reason, and I always felt this way after receiving bad news. I just needed to be outdoors, so I chose to go and see my horse instead which helped calm me as I began trying to process the day's events.

I was certainly glad I was at least able to take the first steps in moving on and to start trying to put it behind me. I'd been up the field for about an hour when my phone rang: it was the hospital telling me they'd forgotten to do a Covid test and that I'd need to go back within the next hour, or the surgery wouldn't be able to go ahead. Really? I was already completely exhausted but now needed to drive thirty minutes back to the hospital to have it completed and as quickly as possible. Luckily, I managed, but I was cursing the whole way. Later on, after finally getting home, I made myself a tea and just sat on the sofa staring into space. I was completely and utterly exhausted, not just in my body and mind but with life in general.

I just never seemed to get over my fatigue and every evening was spent from 3 a.m. to 5 a.m' wide awake, my mind racing with thoughts about what my future looked like, my relationship, life with or without children, then on to work and then I'd be stressing about how I wasn't able to get back to sleep as I could hear the whirring of cars past my window.

I was also determined this time not to resort to alcohol to numb any pain and take the edge off. I wasn't a big drinker and didn't drink regularly, but when coping with major life events, it was an old familiar friend helping me through. Deep down I knew it would only be delaying the emotions and feelings that I needed to feel. I had to experience raw pain to fully heal from it otherwise I'd only be delaying the process.

I decided to try to read in bed with my comfy PJs and blankets. There's something about comfy PJs, dressing gowns and fluffy blankets with a hot drink that really helps to make life better. It helped. I actually started to relax for the first time all day. It was nice to have the space to process everything in my mind. Peter came in and asked if I wanted to discuss anything and I said I didn't. He asked me what I needed and if I was hungry, but I needed someone to literally tell me what decisions to make right now as my mind was all over the place. I said I just needed space and didn't feel up to talking.

He didn't leave. Instead, he insisted that we needed to discuss 'the elephant in the room' regarding the future and IVF as we'd now found ourselves in a new position we hadn't been in before. All the embryos were now used up and we didn't have any process to fall back on. In the past, having a plan B had helped us navigate through each loss. I said I just needed to get through the next few days to get stronger and prepare for surgery. He said he didn't know what my thoughts were in terms of trying in the future but he was 'super reluctant' to go through the IVF process again and that the last few years had just been filled with disappointments.

Well, at least I knew where he stood, but it probably wasn't the best time to announce it. I already was trying to process so much in my mind and didn't have the capacity to take on anything else. But clearly he needed to get it off his chest in case I thought we'd jump in for a new round of IVF. I definitely didn't think that. I always appreciate honesty, and Peter always said right at the beginning he wasn't going to invest a lot of time and money into IVF, so I was always aware it wasn't a long-term route he wanted to pursue. It had been hard enough to get him on board with the last cycle.

I didn't want to fight for it. I didn't want to continue IVF with someone who didn't want to do it as it would only lead to resentments and breakups further down the line. I didn't want to express my thoughts and feelings at this point as the day had been far too long and stressful to consider the future, and I knew I was in no state of mind to even think about IVF, fertility, babies or anything in between.

What I needed once again was to heal and get my strength back to make good decisions from the best place mentally. I knew it was a conversation that was needed sometime soon as there was an elephant in the room that had become impossible to ignore. Honestly, I couldn't see a way forward with two people on completely different pages with different ideas about their future. I knew, deep down, I wasn't ready to hang up my boots yet. I hadn't exhausted all possibilities and I still had hope and fight in me left. But perhaps we were just meant to take different paths.

It was hurtful to admit, but I also didn't want to stand in the way of Peter finding happiness and having children with someone else without having to go through the painful IVF process each time. I wanted to have a life with children in whichever way that came either through IVF, doing it alone, with a partner who wanted children as much as I did and would endure potentially multiple rounds of IVF (which takes a special person I know) or even adoption as I had a lot of hope and faith this might work out for me.

I felt during this time of finding out about the loss that I was also mourning my relationship at the same time as I knew deep down which way this was going to go, and it was really important that we stayed true to ourselves and our dreams for our futures individually. Maybe we would be able to find a way together where we would both be happy without either one of us compromising too much. Who knows? I'm also a firm believer that people come into your life for a reason, to teach you something or for you to teach them something. Either way, a lesson is always learnt. In my relationship, I'd learnt patience and to respect differing opinions and courage.

Our relationship had been filled with losses pretty much the entire time we'd been together. It's a huge strain for any couple to endure. But through losses come vulnerability, strength, hope, courage, love and compassion. By the time I finish this book, I may have a completely different life. Who knows? I'm anxious, hopeful, intrigued and excited about what the future might bring. I've no idea how the story will end or what life will look like if it turns out that we go our separate ways and I'd be living on my own. But with that also comes strength and independence, and I've done that scenario a few times. Or perhaps we'll lay our cards on the table and find a way forward together with children somehow still in the picture.

In a relationship, sometimes you can lose a sense of who you are, not intentionally but because when two people come together you naturally combine everything together. At this time, I'm focused on taking each day as it comes.

THIRTY-FOUR
Exploring Options

'What is meant for you, won't pass you by'

It might sound funny, but when I went through my first miscarriage and multiple losses of loved ones in one month, I felt at such a loss that I went to see a clairvoyant. A clairvoyant is like a psychic who can give answers on things in life and clarification on things you're unsure about and to give you the spiritual reason of why things happen. I know it's very woo-woo and I know a lot of you who are more of the logical mind will immediately say 'what a load of trash', but it's always important in life to keep an open mind.

Earlier in the book, if you remember, I mentioned that I felt as though I had awakened during one of my surgeries. I asked the doctors if I had, but they insisted that there was no way I could have woken up. I didn't mention anything about my life or pregnancies, losses or surgeries during the one-to-one reading, as you should never tell a clairvoyant about your life as it's their job to pick up on things themselves. Also, word of warning, there are so many fakes out there pretending to be gifted when in actual fact, they have no clue about your life and are complete charlatans. If you ever think about having a reading yourself, unless you've had a recommendation, don't waste your money.

Anyway, back to the story. The clairvoyant picked up on my surgery and my sense of loss at the time. He also cottoned on to the fact that I'd lost a lot of blood during my ectopic episode, so much so that he explained I was very close to passing over (dying) and was pretty much over on the other side, which would explain why I felt as though I had woken up for a few minutes. Perhaps my soul was trying to leave my body until I had the blood transfer to stabilise me. This would tally with other cases of out-of-body experiences reported by people who were close to death, or whose heart stopped beating for a few minutes, before they were brought back to life. Either that or I'm basically nuts and just had a very lucid dream!

He said I was very lucky to be here now. I feel that too, as I did lose a lot of blood and ectopic pregnancy is the leading cause of death in pregnancies. It is very rare for it to get to that stage, though, so don't panic. He also exclaimed that the reason the pregnancy failed on a spiritual level was that my body wasn't strong enough at the time to carry it. I'd had so many surgeries and ectopic pregnancies in such short succession, and three surgeries in a year with two being three months apart followed by a gruelling IVF procedure where I was pumped full of drugs, so I understood why my body probably wasn't ready. He went on to say I would have children of my own, two in fact, so perhaps I'll write another book if that prediction comes true!

There are many reasons why losses happen and there are spiritual and scientific theories behind this, and also depending on which category of belief you accept. It's okay to believe in either. I'm going to list the main reasons for both. But, a lot of the time, we're never given a reason why, which as I mentioned earlier, really needs to change.

THIRTY-FIVE
Spiritual Reasons For Losses

'And then I heard the angel say, your baby is always by your side'

If you are sceptical of spiritual explanations, feel free to skip this chapter.

A spiritual understanding of souls suggests that each soul has a purpose and mission which explains why they're coming to Earth. Sometimes their experience is only for a very short time, and they only planned to be in the womb to experience it, or to test the waters, before they came down for a longer duration.

Sometimes souls come for a very short time to let the mother know they can get pregnant or to give reassurance, but for some reason, it's not the right time, either for the mother or the soul, for the soul to remain. It needs to be the right time on both sides.

Sometimes a soul stays around you, waiting for the right time to return.

There are many souls with high vibrational energy that are looking for an enlightening experience in this world. They are waiting for the right single person or couple to have a very specific intention about the kind of child they want, so they feel welcomed into this world. However, if you have an overly specific intention, that will prevent other souls from coming to you who are not the type of child you are seeking.

Don't be discouraged if you have waited a long time for your child to come into this world. That may be a sign that you are on the right path if you only go a little further. When we accept that we are open to anyone coming to us, there are a lot more options, so it might encourage souls to appear more quickly than when we get overly specific about what we are looking for. We might need to refine our expectations first to reap the rewards. (Don't compare your journey with others around you. You are unique, special, and totally worthy of becoming a parent.—Leahirby.com)

Either way, a soul chose you as their mother even if it's only for a very short time. Some beliefs suggest that souls stay with you even if they don't come back down to Earth, so they're always with you even if you can't see or touch them.

Mustard Seed Story

(You don't need to be a Buddhist to take something from this story)

The loss of a pregnancy, while shockingly painful, can make you feel very isolated. It's easy to fall into the trap of thinking you are alone on this journey. One of the best-known Buddhist stories, the parable of the mustard seed, illustrates this point precisely.

A woman whose only child dies is overwhelmed with grief, and in her great suffering, she goes to the Buddha for help. To her relief, he says that he can indeed help her, but before he does so she must bring him a single mustard seed from a house that has not known death. As the woman searches from one house to the next, she realizes that such a place does not exist, because the death of a loved one is an inescapable reality for everyone. In that flash of illumination, the woman recognizes that the pain she is feeling is or will become familiar to everyone. Her experience is fundamentally knowable by others. The misperception of separateness from others dissolves. Her despair begins to heal. (Tricycle.org)

THIRTY-SIX
Scientific Reasons Behind Loss

*'You never arrived in my arms, but
you will never leave my heart'*

If you're of a logical mind and find spiritualism too hippy-like and not for you, here are the scientific explanations to account for loss:

❖ The majority of miscarriage cases
   are due to random genetic errors
   and chromosomes that make normal
   foetal development impossible

❖ In about half of cases, genetic testing
   of the remains of a miscarriage re-
   veals no chromosomal abnormality

❖ 1 in 5 pregnancies end in miscarriage,
   but many women will go on to have a
   healthy pregnancy; only 5% are recurrent

❖ Structural problem in the uterus, such as an abnormal wall, or septum, dividing the space, or noncancerous growths called fibroids or cervix issues

❖ Thyroid issues, hormonal imbalances

❖ Clotting disorders

❖ Extreme stress such as the death of a loved one, etc.

❖ Lifestyle factors i.e. drinking and/or smoking

❖ Chronic illnesses

❖ Women older than 35 have a higher risk of miscarriage than do younger women. At 35, you have about a 20% risk. At 40, the risk is about 40%. And at 45, it's about 80%

❖ Women who have had two or more consecutive miscarriages are at higher risk of miscarriage.

❖ Weight: women overweight can be more at risk of miscarriages

- ❖ Blocked tubes can cause ectopic pregnancies

- ❖ Natural killer cells

- ❖ Inflammation creating a hostile environment

Sometimes, there's just no reason that explains scientifically why loss happens. I'm a huge fan of having immunology testing done and getting your reproductive system checked to make sure that everything is in good working order. But, bear in mind, conditions can be perfect, embryos seemingly 'top grade' and you can still potentially come up against issues.

THIRTY-SEVEN
Options To Conceive

There are always choices, even if it's not what you'd envisioned for yourself. You don't have to give up your dream completely if it hasn't been working out the way you expected. Here are some options depending on the issue:

❖ Sperm donation

❖ Egg donation

❖ Embryo donation

❖ Surrogacy

❖ Adoption

❖ Fostering

There may be more, but these are the main routes for singles or couples to explore. Also, in this day and age, you don't need to be with a partner to conceive. It's all down to your own personal choice as to what fits for you, but there are options. It's also completely understandable if you feel you've reached the end of the road and decide either by yourself or as a couple that you don't want to try again and are choosing to live a life without children.

You'll find a list of helpful websites and support groups to assist and support at the end of the book.

It's important when TTC (trying to conceive) to have an outlet for stress and ways to stay sane. It tests your mental strength to the limit. Do find a way of sharing your feelings and joining a community online, talking to friends and trying to keep life as normal as possible amidst all the chaos. If you decide to end fertility treatment for whatever reason, don't ever feel like you have to explain your reasons to anyone. Many have gone on to live fulfilled lives without children and found other things in life to fulfil them. If you're unsure, then remember there are options and take the time to think it through to be sure of your decision as it's not an easy one to make.

For those of you suffering loss or in waiting hell, feeling like your life is on hold, I had some words of wisdom come to me whilst lying in bed one night waiting for the outcome of my latest pregnancy which, as you know, didn't go to plan. It was needed for myself too at a time where I needed words of comfort, so perhaps it can help you too when you're struggling to find the happiness in your life and feeling a bit lost.

Even In Darkness You Can Find The Light

It's okay not to be okay sometimes. It's okay to shut yourself off from the world, shut the curtains, hide under the duvet and heal your soul. *But don't stay in that place too long.*

It's okay to push away support if you only need your own company for a while. *But don't keep everyone locked out.*

It's okay to accept help from people, let them. *You don't have to be strong all of the time and do this alone.* It will help your healing to allow others to pick you up and it will make them feel good too.

It's okay not to smile even if something is funny but you can't manage it.

It's okay to feel like you're acting the part of someone else every time you step outdoors, putting on a front to the world even though you're one wrong word away from breaking down inside. This is loss. This is real. This is healing. *Allow it, but don't stay in the dark too long.*

Soon you'll wake up one morning and you won't need to act like you're the strong person you're trying to be. You WILL be that strong person again, telling your words of wisdom to someone else that needs to hear your story and kind words to lift them up and help them heal in the same way you did.

THIRTY-EIGHT

Things to help during fertility treatment:

- ❖ Regular walks in nature

- ❖ Meditate

- ❖ Spa days (if you're not in treatment)

- ❖ Meeting up with friends and family

- ❖ Yoga

- ❖ Avoid people who never say the right things and/or are unsupportive

- ❖ Have a backup plan if treatment isn't successful

- ❖ Decide on an end goal and timeline

- ❖ Avoid pregnant friends, etc., if it will trigger you—be kind to yourself

- ❖ List all the things you couldn't do pregnant if a cycle fails and do them!

- ❖ Talk to a fertility therapist—this is important

- ❖ Listen to uplifting music and watch funny movies

- ❖ Being aware if you're becoming obsessed with anything fertility related

- ❖ Regular date nights with partner, or friend nights if single, without discussing fertility issues or anything related to it

- ❖ Gym

- ❖ Clear your schedule if your cycle fails

- ❖ Write a list of goals and dreams in life outside of TTC

- ❖ Positive affirmations

- ❖ Share your story on a forum or start a blog

❖ Respond to others posting for guidance with something you have experience of

❖ Stay off anything to do with TTC or IVF forums online if getting too much

❖ Keep a journal—you may want to write your own book one day

❖ Rest and eat well

❖ Get home help if you're low on energy

❖ Consider who you'll tell when starting IVF cycle and decide when you're ready who/when you'll tell if it's unsuccessful

❖ IVF is a numbers game, for every unsuccessful story there are plenty of successful ones

❖ Read stories of hope and success if you need to be lifted

THIRTY-NINE
Ways to Cope with Loss

'We must be willing to let go of the life we have planned, so as to have the life that is waiting for us'
—Joseph Campbell

The above quote has never rung so true to me as it does now. It sums up exactly where I am in my fertility journey. There is no right, single way to deal with the bad news of loss and it's different for each person. For me, I found doing something personal to mark the life of my baby helpful and I would visit church to say a prayer and light a candle.

I would keep myself busy and throw myself into work, but there have also been other times where I've completely cleared my schedule and taken time out which helped too. I've shared my emotions with my partner and closest friends, but there have been other times where I've kept it to myself until I was strong enough to talk about it and try again.

I always found being out in nature helped, and even on the days I didn't feel like it, I still went for a walk. The one thing that did help every time was to share my story on forums and read the stories of others too, which I found comfort in. This book has really helped me to heal past traumas, especially with my ruptured ectopic pregnancy. Not knowing I was pregnant until I was nearly dying will always stay with me, although the pain has lessened over time.

I firmly believe in giving back and helping others when you're ready by starting a blog, writing a book or posting your story in forums and support groups. Your words can really help others to heal too. This process is hard enough to try to face alone and your words can help inspire, heal and change someone's world, which will have a positive domino effect and empower each person to speak up and use their voice to end the silence and stigma around trying to conceive and pregnancy loss as many of us have experienced it.

There is nothing to be ashamed about in this, only strength to be gained for having experienced it. Life is all about experience. The good and the bad. The light and the dark. We may get our rainbows, we may not but either way, we have grown and have a story to inspire and heal.

I'm pretty certain each and every one of you has become a different person on this journey of heart-break and loss. I know I have, but I've also been lucky to meet some of the most compassionate, courageous, determined, awe-inspiring, empathetic, resilient IVF warriors along the way.

You may or may not have a few stars and rainbows in the sky that you hold dear forever, but you will have found a deep level of compassion in humanity you didn't know existed from these warrior ladies in this secret fertility club. There is a strength within that could rival even the world's strongest man, a bond of sisterhood your closest friends couldn't understand, and a life experience that you could never learn anywhere else. That alone is worth it. Would I choose to go through all of this again for the chance of holding my baby in my arms? Yes, I probably would.

Here are some ideas that may help with loss:

- ❖ Decide on attending a memorial for your baby

- ❖ Have plenty of support on when your due date would've been

- ❖ Clear your schedule and allow time to grieve

- ❖ Rest, rest and more rest!

- ❖ Let others help you emotionally, and with chores too

- ❖ Don't let go of hope if you still want a baby

- ❖ Don't let anyone talk you out of your
  dream if you still want to try

- ❖ Offer to volunteer at a baby loss
  charity. Giving back is healing

- ❖ Share your story, even if it's
  done anonymously

- ❖ Help someone else who's struggling
  too, once you're strong enough

- ❖ Use the support info included by
  joining an online community

- ❖ Stay off TTC forums and stay away
  from anything pregnancy-related

- ❖ Stay away from social media if
  it will trigger you with pregnancy ads or announcements

❖ Avoid friends who are pregnant, baby showers, etc., until you're strong enough and don't feel guilty. You need to be kind and put yourself first right now

❖ Try not to drown yourself in alcohol or even worse, drugs, as it may feel better momentarily, but it's a depressant and will make you feel 1000x worse the next day and drain you of the energy needed to heal

❖ Take time out and really feel your emotions, no matter how hard, as it's part of the healing process. If you push the feelings down or try to avoid them, they will keep coming up until you've dealt with them and this will only delay the grieving process. Cry as many times and for as long as you need to, but don't feel bad if you can't cry as everyone processes grief differently

❖ You will also grieve for the dreams and life you had planned which was pulled from right underneath you. A loss doesn't mean you have to give up that dream or hope of having it

❖ When you're strong enough, put a plan together of your next steps for trying again if that's what you want to do

❖ Write a list of all the things you enjoy doing and all the things you couldn't do when pregnant and tick them off. It will help you to bring fun and joy back into your life

❖ Book a holiday and a change of scene in the sun, or anywhere you desire. Time away will help

❖ Make sure the hospital knows to cancel any further appointments or letters for that pregnancy as it's heart-breaking to receive them through the door after a loss

❖ Be kind to yourself no matter what and talk to yourself like you would to your best friend if she was struggling to get through

❖ See a professional therapist who specialises in pregnancy loss

❖ Create memories for your baby

❖ Make your own decisions and your own timeline for healing unapologetically

❖ Talk and share your feelings with your partner and remember they will deal with grief differently to you and may perhaps seem like they aren't show-ing any emotion, but they just process feelings differently and perhaps don't show or talk about their feelings in the same way you do, but it doesn't mean they're feeling any less then you are

❖ You may feel resentment towards your partner for not having experienced the physical trauma too. This is normal and, during the grieving process, we look for things to blame. It will pass and each emotion is part of the healing process

There is a process to grieving which is as follows:

Denial: At first, it might be impos-sible to grasp what's hap-pened. You might find your-self in shock or disbelief.

Guilt: You might wonder if you could have done anything to avoid the pregnancy loss.

Anger: No matter what caused your loss, you might be angry at yourself, your spouse or partner, your doctor, or a higher power. You might also feel angry at the unfairness of your loss.

Depression: You might develop symptoms of depression—loss of interest or pleasure in normal activities, changes in eating or sleeping habits, and trouble concentrating and making decisions.

Envy: You might intensely envy expectant parents. It might suddenly seem like babies and pregnant women are everywhere you look.

Yearning: You might experience feelings of deep or anxious longing and desire to be with your baby. You might also imagine what you would be doing with your baby now. (Mayo Clinic)

Eventually, you reach acceptance and after enough time you will heal, even though at first it seems like you'll never move past it. Remember others around you, who are on the journey with you, might also be grieving.

They might say some insensitive comments such as:

> *'Well at least you weren't that far along.'*
>
> *'It's only cells at this stage anyway.'*
>
> *'It obviously wasn't meant to be.'*
>
> *'There's always adoption, have you considered that?'*
>
> *'Well, at least you already have a child.'*
>
> *'You can always try again.'*

Either change the subject or tell them you don't want to discuss it. You don't have to accept or take on board other people's opinions and they are just that—opinions.

FORTY
Stories Of Hope

*'Hope is being able to see that there is
light despite all of the darkness'*

I always think that it's important to remember to keep
hope after a loss, especially when you want to continue
trying. Don't forget, many couples and single parents have
had success even after spending many years trying. We
never know what our timeline will be, but in the hardest
of times, it's inspiring to read others' stories and draw
strength from them. Here's a few I wanted to share with
you.

Success After 8 Rounds IVF and
multiple miscarriages

An article in the Huffington post described how
doctors discovered the mother-to-be had blocked tubes
and recommended she underwent her first round of
IVF at a fertility centre. It worked; she became pregnant.
The couple were thrilled. But their joy soon turned to

heartache as they lost the baby very soon after the embryo was implanted. They went on to have seven rounds of IVF, each one resulting in pregnancy—only for the embryo not to survive beyond eight weeks. The mother-to-be described the pain as incomprehensible.

Eventually she was tested and the results revealed that she was carrying a 'translocation of chromosomes', medically known as Robertsonian translocation of chromosomes 15 and 22, a rare condition that doesn't affect the mother's own health, so she'd had no idea. However, it was being passed on, leading to an imbalance in her embryos. After PGT testing a healthy embryo was implanted and their healthy baby was born.

73-Year-Old Becomes Oldest Ever Mother in the World!

The BBC reported the claim of doctors in India where a 73-year-old woman reportedly gave birth to twin girls.

Doctors in the east Indian state of Andhra Pradesh claimed the woman's age makes her the world's oldest women ever to give birth after they allegedly delivered the twins by caesarean section following successful IVF treatment.

The mother told BBC Telugu: 'It is the happiest time of my life.' And quoted by the Indo-Asian News Service, she said: 'God has answered our prayers.' She claimed to have seen many doctors before she and her husband found success.

Her age meant that she could not release eggs and therefore donor eggs were used which were fertilized by her husband's sperm. She fell pregnant after the first cycle and gave birth to healthy twins.

The baby born after 22 years of parental infertility

An article in the Daily Mail told the story of couple who tried to get pregnant for twenty-two years. Along the way, they adopted two children. When the lady missed her period, she figured she was starting menopause. Seven pregnancy tests later, she came to the conclusion that her dream of getting pregnant had finally come true, at age forty-three. In April, she gave birth to a healthy baby girl with her new husband.

Miracle Baby Born After 13 Miscarriages

The Independent newspaper carried the story of a mother of a 'miracle' baby. The child was born after thirteen miscarriages. The mother said she hoped her story would inspire strength in other women who are struggling to give birth.

She had experienced eleven miscarriages in the first trimester. Two pregnancies were lost at seventeen and twenty weeks.

After trying multiple trials and treatments to overcome fertility issues, the mother-to-be and her husband had said their fourteenth attempt would be their final one. By this time two conditions had been identified which were impacting her ability to maintain a pregnancy.

She was initially treated with folic acid to address antiphospholipid syndrome—also known as 'sticky blood syndrome'—which can increase the risk of pregnancy loss. Using drugs to improve the lining of her uterus and powerful steroids to suppress her immune system. The pregnancy passed the critical twenty-four-week threshold, where premature babies have the best chance of survival. Her baby is healthy and thriving.

A mother conceives quadruplets from four separate eggs

Redbook magazine reported the case of a twenty-eight-year-old mother who was diagnosed with polycystic ovary syndrome (PCOS) and told she could never get pregnant. To everyone's astonishment, she learned she was having non-identical quadruplets, which happens in about one out of every 700,000 pregnancies. Despite weighing only two or three pounds each at birth, her sons and daughters were safely delivered and are now perfectly healthy infants.

Miracle Babies Born Weeks Apart After Mum and Surrogate Get Pregnant at Same Time

A report from Good Morning America related the case of a couple, expecting a baby via surrogate, welcomed not one, but two children after the mother became pregnant at the same time as her surrogate.

The couple had had trouble getting pregnant. They married in 2013 and began IVF in 2014, but the embryos were not implanting. Their neighbour, already a mother of one, stepped in and offered herself as a surrogate. On February 20, 2018, she underwent an embryo transfer. Within a week, the surrogate learned she was pregnant with their child.

Then the couple announced that one day later, the mum—who had been told that she would never conceive—startlingly found herself pregnant via natural conception.

Now, the delighted couple are parents to two children, who were born twenty-four days apart.

Miracle Of Mother Who Gave Birth
To A 9 Month Ectopic Pregnancy

Another report from the Daily Mail records that doctors are calling a child a 'miracle baby'. The little girl was delivered alive and well after growing in her mother's ovary instead of the womb.

For nine months, the couple were completely unaware their baby was anything but normal. It was only during the birth, at just before full term, that midwives realised they were dealing with a medical phenomenon.

Her parents have called the little girl 'Durga' meaning Goddess to reflect the miracle of her birth.

British experts say the chances of a baby being carried for so long in this way and both mother and child surviving unharmed are a million to one. An ovarian pregnancy is one of the rarest variations of ectopic—or out of the womb—pregnancies, which can have life-threatening consequences for the mother. It was a miracle that the mother's ovary did not stretch and break, which could have caused deadly internal bleeding.

This is indeed a medical phenomenon.

Mother of Seven with Polycystic Ovary
Syndrome and Endometriosis Reveals

She Endured Six Miscarriages Before Welcoming Miracle Quadruplets

The website Babygaga.com carried the story of a mother who suffered from fertility issues such as polycystic ovary syndrome and endometriosis. The woman had six miscarriages before successfully giving birth to her quadruplets thanks to hormone injections which helped stimulate her ovaries.

Diagnosed with endometriosis, a condition where tissue usually found in the lining of the womb grows in other parts of the body and sometimes causes fertility issues, doctors were confident she would still be able to conceive.

With no immediate plans for more children, it only became an issue six years later when the mother-to-be had her first miscarriage so early in her pregnancy that she had not even known she was expecting.

Conceiving again shortly afterwards, in 2002, the couple were delighted when their child was born. In 2005, when their child was around three, the couple began discussing giving her a sibling. They had no idea that it would be eleven long years before baby number three came along.

They fell pregnant in around August 2005, soon after they began trying, but, just eight weeks later, another miscarriage occurred. After that the woman experienced problems conceiving, and after eight months of trying, she sought advice from her doctor. Tests revealed that she was having a severe endometriosis flare-up.

The first line of treatment was a laparoscopy, where a tiny telescope was inserted into her abdomen before surgeons made small incisions to cut out the patches of endometriosis. Over the years, she also tried various fertility treatments including clomiphene—a drug that encourages the release of an egg every month—all to no avail.

She had several investigatory tests to try to determine the underlying cause of her issues. She discovered that she had low levels of the hormone progesterone, which prepares the body for potential pregnancy after ovulation. She was also diagnosed with polycystic ovary syndrome (PCOS)—a hormonal condition making natural conception difficult.

Further tests showed up that the left side of her womb was weakened and damaged by endometriosis and that the PCOS had left some cysts on her ovaries which were too small to surgically remove. Essentially, her body could no longer prepare itself for pregnancy.

In 2012, following injections at the fertility clinic, the mother discovered she was expecting again. This time, she carried her baby to full term, and her son arrived in February 2013. Returning, at a later date, to the same fertility clinic that had helped the couple before, the mother began follistim and progesterone injections again - conceiving after just two months, only for a bombshell to be dropped at her six-week scan; she was expecting sextuplets.

In the end two of the foetuses did not make it to full term, but the mother gave birth to four healthy babies who have gone on to grow into healthy children.

FORTY-ONE
Looking to the Future

'The Best Is Yet to Come'

I'm now in recovery after my surgical management for my second miscarriage. I'm not sure what the future will bring, but I'm hopeful and I certainly won't be giving up on my dream to mother a child. At the moment, it's a time for healing and remembering the other things in life I have around me that also fulfil me, such as friends, family, animals, and my businesses.

Writing this book has truly been a healing journey for me. It has helped me through my most recent loss and also helped me to make sense of the rollercoaster journey members of the secret fertility club undergo! I do hope I've helped at least someone out there to find solace and strength in my words as we're going through it all together as one.

We're never alone in this, and I invite each and every one of you to please speak up. Use your voice and share your stories of loss, struggles, hope and remembrance of your little ones which will not only help you but will help pick up others too when they need to hear your stories the most. It's through sharing that we find strength and healing.

I've set up a Facebook support group at @SecretFertilityClub and I encourage you to share on here, offer advice to others, ask questions and get actively involved. Help to raise awareness of the causes that brought us to this club but, remember, through these struggles that we are warriors. We have persevered and pushed through the battles when everything has been against us and still came out fighting. That takes a special kind of person. I feel honoured to be a part of the Fertility Club through which we knock down the walls of secrecy and break the code of silence to help one another to heal.

That's what life is truly about.

EPILOGUE
Jumping To The Here And Now

Since I wrote this book, the relationship with my partner sadly ended. We were simply on different pages and seeing the future in incompatible ways. There are no hard feelings though, and we wish one another well.

After my breakup, I moved to a new town out in the countryside. It was hard, at first, to leave my friends, but there were also advantages. I am now closer to my family, and it gave me a much-needed fresh start and time to heal. My career has gone from strength to strength. I won Vocal Professional Of The Year, was nominated for Music Supervisor Of The Year and signed a publishing deal for my book.

I am now with someone new. We've been together for just under a year and it's going really well. We met through work, and I think it really helped that we knew each other for a few years first. We had no idea that we would end up together, especially as a relationship was the last thing on my mind. I don't want to say too much as I want to see where it goes but I am very happy and positive about what the future might bring. He has played a huge part in helping me to heal from everything I'd been through.

Before we got together, I decided fostering was something I really wanted to try. It was a big decision to take on a child on my own without a partner but I felt ready for the challenge. (The real reason I decided to start my fostering journey in hindsight was a reaction to the baby I had lost and a need to fill that gap in my life.) I'm going to delve into what the whole experience was like for me to:

A. Give an honest view of my personal experience for anyone considering fostering

and

B. To try to process what the hell has happened as a bomb went off in my life when I received my first foster child placement, gulp! This is the only way I can describe the past few months as a six-year-old girl suddenly landed in my life on a normal Tuesday afternoon.

Let's go back to the beginning. It took around six months to be approved as a foster carer and the process is VERY invasive. The social worker assigned to your application needs to know EVERYTHING about you since birth and all the places you've lived and who with (turns out I've moved nearly thirty times in my life.) Trying to remember dates and addresses was nearly harder than the actual fostering. I had weekly talks over the phone with the social worker discussing my life and it was like a therapy session rolled into one without having to pay £100 p/h: result. It was difficult having to delve into my losses and my last breakup at the time as it was felt like she was opening the wounds, but it was necessary. Another reason I wanted to foster was because I had lived with my best friend and her family at the age of fifteen for a few years for reasons I won't go into (otherwise it would turn into a biopic, and no-one wants that). I felt like I wanted to give something back as it had helped me all those years ago.

Whilst qualifying as a foster carer, you also need to complete what feels like many hours of training while you're being assessed to see who is cut out for the job (not that they tell you that but this is what it's really about). Not many are as it turns out.

The scariest part was they also needed to interview EX BOYFRIENDS!!! Who needs that? Luckily, at that point, time had passed and Peter and I weren't wanting to bury one another under the patio floors any more so it went well, and he wrote me a nice reference—I mean why wouldn't he? I'm a perfect girlfriend—OK, perfect in my mind anyway.

They also interview your family and friends, which is understandable. Once you've passed that stage, and haven't dropped out already or haven't been outed as a secret serial killer on weekends, they then make a visit to your house to do a risk assessment which involves pointing out all the things wrong with it which you then need to fix and have in place even down to locking knives away etc. Crazy, right? By this stage you are starting to think, what exactly am I letting myself in for?

Once your assessment gets to the panel you're pretty much already approved and it's a great milestone to reach as many people don't make it that far. Once I was at this stage, things started to get fairly serious with my new partner and I wanted to see where it could go. I'd had no inkling that we might become an item when I first applied for fostering but, my oh my, life does happen when you're busy making other plans.

I started freaking out, as I was enjoying my new relationship and my partner was already living quite a distance away. Not only that, but all my friends chose this time to suddenly come out of the woodwork and make me face a brutal reality by telling me that I simply wasn't ready to take on the needs of a challenging child when I was still healing. I was literally days away from panel to see if I'd be approved as a foster carer frantically trying to decide what to do. My friends had a point. Bloody friends—why do they have to make you see the things you want to avoid? But equally I'd just spent the best part of six months working towards this to just throw it all away.

I rang my social worker the night before and laid it on the line, 'I can't do this,' I blurted out frantically.

'Can't do what?' she laughed. 'You've already done all the work and you only need to show up to panel.'

'No, I can't foster I'm simply not ready.'

'But you've been adamant all along you're ready for this.'

I explained yes that's how I felt in that moment and the truth of the matter has only just hit me hard in the face. She told me to go through panel as normal, don't mention a thing about this and perhaps do emergency fostering. (This is when a child turns up suddenly having just been removed from their home for safety reasons until they find a placement (home) or respite (temporary fostering for a few days to give carers a break.) I felt a lot better knowing I could perhaps do a few days rather than a few years.

The panel went well and I was approved. Yay! They had all read my 90-page report (known in the foster world as form-f) on my life story which I'd dedicated many hours to writing up with my social worker. I was happy and training continued, as you must complete three hours a week of 'Mandatory Foster Training' for one year after getting approved.

This covers safeguarding, emergency first aid, medication and health care, health and safety in the home, managing challenging behaviour and safer caring. You are then assigned a social worker who visits you every four to six weeks and the child's social worker if you have a child full time along with many other meetings you undertake when fostering full-time.

I received lots of referrals for children who needed homes long term and there are hundreds that the local authority receives on a daily basis which is sad. I eventually started doing respite for a married couple who were looking after two siblings, both girls, aged six and seven. The first girl I looked after for a weekend was very outgoing, loud and full-on. She couldn't sit still very long so I planned lots of fun activities including an adventure barn and a trip to see my pony.

She was fine until it was time to go to school then she was adamant she wasn't going. We eventually got passed that when I said, 'Well you are going,' and carried on getting ready. The next respite was for her sister who seemed very sweet and bubbly. She was only six. Again, we planned lots of fun things and she loved to lie-in on a morning which was perfect for me.

I knew a little bit of background on these children but you're never told too much, but like most that get placed through agencies they are trickier to place than the children with the local authority. (The local authority is always the first port of call when finding homes for children. If they struggle to place them for whatever reason the fostering agencies will then look to find homes for them.)

A lot of these children have been through a lot of trauma and many have been through severe neglect and abuse on many different levels—violence, drugs/ alcohol—that most people don't see in a lifetime, so parenting is approached in a more therapeutic way rather than in a traditional sense.

It was just after the Christmas period when I received a call from the agency saying that *Caitlyn needed to move suddenly from the foster home she was in and I felt I'd built a bond with her so didn't want her to end up with someone she didn't know somewhere far away in the UK. The issue was that I was only given twenty-four hours to make a decision due to circumstances at the foster placement she was in.

I discussed it with my partner who seemed supportive but ultimately wanted the decision to come from me. Deep down I knew it would have an impact on our relationship. But my family encouraged me to take her on and lots of friends said they would step in and offer help when needed, and so I figured what's the worst that could happen? I have the support and it could change a child's life. Isn't that the point of fostering?

The first few weeks were like a honeymoon period. I really enjoyed getting her room ready with all her things that had been dropped off prior to her arrival, making it nice with all her teddies out and lots of girly pink things. The plan was to drive Caitlyn each way to drop her to school and pick up while she transitioned and moved to a school more local to me which seemed fine at the time. I didn't know then that it would take four hours out of my day and started to really exhaust me, along with trying to run my business at the same time. It was already getting too much on a physical level in just the first few weeks

Just to cap it all, I came down with Covid and was very ill with flu-type symptoms and then—BOOM! Just like that the honeymoon period between Caitlyn and I was over. Lying on the sofa one weekend, I was subjected to the most horrific screams I'd ever encountered outside of a horror film. Not what you need with body chills, fever and a headache not too dissimilar from the kind or hangovers you'd endure after a crate of Prosecco.

OK...now I knew why in fostering they call it the 'honeymoon period'.

'You fucker!' she screamed. 'I'm going to kill you!' OK...this is next level. I removed myself and let her calm down and wrote it off as perhaps she was over-tired. I didn't really want to question where her colourful language came from at this stage. But that day I got an insight into how life was to become for the next few months—sweet child for a few days then screams and abuse that would last sometimes up to two hours at a time including trying to attack me and damage my things (luckily six-year-old punches aren't particularly damaging).

There wasn't even really much you could do as you have to be careful how you 'restrain' foster children and I was told to block any attacks and put away any expensive things until she settled. Fine...I'll just convert my rooms into padded cells, shall I? I even tried having a relaxing bath through it one evening with the loudest screams outside the door mixed in with spa music—not the most soothing bath I've ever had. I also soon learnt all the people who said they'd be there to 'support you with it and would help out' were not there when I needed them. Even trying to find a childminder for an hour was like chasing tumbleweed so I was 100% on my own managing her behaviours in the best way I could while trying to find the energy to keep my business going every day.

I have maximum respect for single parents and all carers. Not easy—At—All. My partner and I spoke every day and he'd visit when he could but I kept thinking I made this decision, I need to see it through. Many carers say that a child will test you to begin with, especially a child that has experienced many prior placements and moved around multiple schools. They need to test to see if the adults can be trusted, and won't let them down and reject them when their whole life they'd been let down and rejected by the people they trusted the most. (Yes, many times during the exorcist-style screams or threats to kill me, I would try and remind myself of the terrible life she'd had and that it wasn't her fault!)

Eventually though, I was getting to the point of complete burnout and struggling to just make it through each day. I was in complete survival mode, not seeing friends, seeing an impact on my relationship, struggling to work and Caitlyn didn't seem to be settling either. She was lashing out day and night, and the neighbours were also getting fed up with the constant screaming. I knew I had to make a decision—and quickly.

I battled with a lot of guilt and felt I was giving up and contributing to the people in her life who had continually let her down, but equally I knew she needed two carers not one, carers who didn't have other commitments outside of foster care to devote the time she needed.

With a heavy heart, I pulled the plug. I must say once I reached that decision, I felt a massive weight had been lifted. Fostering is an amazing thing to do and really can change a child's life. Every child is different and while my foster child had severe traumas and complex issues that were too much for a single person, it's still one of the most rewarding things you can do. (I have seen the results of where placements do work and the change in the children is incredible.)

In the end, I couldn't commit to the demands of my business and the needs of a child with such complex issues. Caitlyn, as it stands at this point, is waiting on a forever home and I truly hope she finds it. It's not the children's fault, they have been through so much in their lives that's beyond their control. I also came away with many lessons and an insight into parenting and it was interesting to see how I handled high conflict situations, learning to be completely in the present and offering opportunities she would never have otherwise experienced, such as swimming lessons, horse riding and trips shopping/cinema which is all new to many foster children who often have never even celebrated birthdays. It is very sad when a child discloses information about their previous life as you wish you could do something to fix them or wish they never had to experience that, but sometimes even love alone isn't enough.

I still would like a child of my own eventually, but at the moment its 100% definitely not something I'm looking at right now. I am in the space of having complete gratitude for my life, my freedom, seeing friends, taking on work projects, travelling to the city to see my partner—the simple things. I'm super excited that I've just booked to go to Cannes Film Festival simply because...I can. For work purposes obviously not to hang out on the celebrity yachts and drink champagne! (Although if anyone is offering, I won't pass it up.)

Having kids of your own must be an amazing experience but I've also learnt parenting comes with many restrictions and challenges too and can feel very isolating at times. I feel it's important to live a life you're excited about rather than perhaps thinking a child will fix the things you feel you're missing. I would genuinely be happy to continue living the life I have without 'needing' a child to fill the gaps and if it happens, it happens and if it doesn't then that's truly OK too.

Every cloud has a silver lining.
'Difficult Roads Lead To Beautiful Destinations'

If you enjoyed this book, please consider leaving
a review at the online bookseller of choice.
Thankyou
and don't forget to check out other
Sparsile titles at www.sparsilebooks.com

Resources

ENDING FERTILITY TREATMENT / LIVING A LIFE CHILD FREE:

For Him:

https://www.himfertility.com/

For Her:

https://fertilitynetworkuk.org/

https://www.fertilityfriends.co.uk/

https://www.bica.net/

https://gateway-women.com/

https://www.verywellfamily.com/childfree-life-after-infertility

Resolve.org

Blogs:

Silent Sorority

URL: http://blog.silentsorority.com/

Infertility Honesty

URL: https://infertilityhonesty.com/

Forums:

https://www.inspire.com/groups/finding-a-resolution-for-infertility/

MISCARRIAGE/LOSS:

Tommy's

www.Tommys.org

Miscarriage Association

https://www.miscarriageassociation.org.uk/

PREGNANCY LOSS:

Sands

https://www.sands.org.uk/

Lullaby Trust

lullabytrust.org.uk

Petals Charity

petalscharity.org

Twins Trust

https://twinstrust.org/bereavement

Child Death Helpline

childdeathhelpline.org.uk

Saying Goodbye

sayinggoodbye.org

Life After Loss

lifeafterloss.org.uk

Arc

arc-uk.org

FORUMS FOR LOSS:

For Him:

https://www.thedadsnet.com/forums/topic/dealing-with-loss-fertility-issues-ivf-and-miscarriage/

For Her:

https://www.miscarriageassociation.org.uk/miscarriage-forum/

https://www.madeformums.com/getting-pregnant/rainbow-babies-stories/

Facebook Groups:

- https://www.facebook.com/groups/Pregnanylossstillbirthandmiscarriage

- https://www.facebook.com/groups/261891265038126

- https://www.facebook.com/groups/165605147196880

ECTOPIC PREGNANCY SUPPORT:

https://ectopic.org.uk/ **inc forum**

https://www.ectopicpregnancy.co.uk/

https://www.tommys.org/pregnancy-information/pregnancy-complications/baby-loss/ectopic-pregnancy-information-and-support

Facebook Groups:

- Ectopic pregnancy Support Group

- Ectopic (Tubal) pregnancy and support group

- TTC After an Ectopic Pregnancy

- Pregnant After An Ectopic Or Miscarriage Support Group

FORUMS FOR SUPPORT UNDERGOING TREATMENT:

https://www.fertilityfriends.co.uk/

https://healthunlocked.com/fertility-network-uk

https://www.mumsnet.com/Talk/infertility

https://forum.madeformums.com/

Blogs:

Starbucks, Peace and The Pursuit Of A Baby

URL: http://trialsbringjoy.wordpress.com

No Bun In The Oven

URL: http://nobunintheoven.com

Don't Count Your Eggs

URL: http://www.dontcountyoureggs.typepad.com/

The Two Week Wait

URL: http://the2weekwait.blogspot.com/

More Here: https://www.ivfauthority.com/top-ivf-blogs-forums/

Facebook Groups:

- IVF Worldwide Community

- TTC With Male Factor Infertility

- IVF+40 Plus With Own Eggs

- Trying To Conceive, Infertility and Pregnancy Support Group

- Fertility Support Group

Acknowledgements

Firstly, thanks to Lesley Affrossman at Sparsile for signing the book and helping to get my story out into the world to help others. The rest of the team including Alex Winpenny who worked on the editing and Stephen Cashmore who proofread it.

Lastly, to all the people that stood by and supported me through the triumphs and heartbreaks, you know who you are and to all the members of the secret fertility club, with whom I wouldn't have made it through without.

Sparsile Non-Fiction

Titles you may enjoy from our non-fiction range:

Comics and Columbine - Tom Campbell

In this angry, tender, and extraordinary work, Thomas Campbell writes with fierce immediacy from the cultural ultra-violet of the Asperger spectrum, allowing us a crucial glimpse into the emotional gulag to which we thoughtlessly sentence thousands daily, and perhaps moderating our disingenuous surprise when another awkward loner takes an assault rifle to class for Show and Tell.

Once Upon A Blue Moon - Olivia Norfolk

Once Upon A Blue Moon will be Olivia Norfolk's first and final book because Olivia is suffering from a deadly brain tumour which will end her life in the next few months.

Her book is a testament to her courage in the face of oblivion.

Secret Fertility Club - Amelia McCloskey

Welcome to the Secret Fertility Club. A club nobody wants to join, full of women linked by a singular goal – to become parents, despite the obstacles stacked against them. In her book, Amelia McCloskey shines a light on the strength and perseverance of its members.

Science for Heretics - Barrie Condon

SCIENCE IS BROKEN

Science is everywhere, our medicines, our transport, what we eat and drink. Like it or not, we can't make real progress without it. There's just one dilemma ... What if there are profound problems with all aspects of scientific theory and methods?

www.sparsilebooks.com